GradeAid with Practice Tests

for

Baron and Byrne

Social Psychology
Tenth Edition

prepared by

Eric D. Miller
Kent State University

Boston   New York   San Francisco
Mexico City   Montreal   Toronto   London   Madrid   Munich   Paris
Hong Kong   Singapore   Tokyo   Cape Town   Sydney

Copyright © 2003 Pearson Education, Inc.

ISBN 0-205-36649-X

Printed in the United States of America
10 9 8 7 6 5 4 3 2 1   08 07 06 05 04 03 02

TABLE OF CONTENTS

USING YOUR STUDY GUIDE

Your instructor has chosen a classic, internationally respected social psychology text. Most social psychologists regard the Baron and Byrne *Social Psychology* text as one of the best—if not *the best*—in the field. This text will inform you about the exciting and important field of social psychology. I am also confident that you'll find it quite helpful in years to come with respect to your future academic and career endeavors.

This study guide has been designed so that you could get the most of your text. Let me stress a very important point *before* you begin your use of this study aid: ***This study guide is not a substitute for reading your text.*** Only a very risky soul should rely solely on this study guide and expect to master social psychology—let alone receive a good grade. It also should go without saying that this study guide cannot cover every single detail covered in your text— obviously that's why it's so important to read your text! Now, with that behind us, let me say that I truly believe that this study guide will aid your study efforts considerably—and make that cherished "A" a more plausible reality for you. OK, here's the deal about how you should use this study guide…

You will find that there are *four* self-explanatory, distinct sections for each of your thirteen text chapters. The "Before you read" section should literally be reviewed prior to your text reading for that specific chapter. This section highlights the key learning objectives and summarizes the basic issues that the chapter discusses. Think of it as an "intellectual warm-up" before the "big read."

Now, the "As you read" section will be most effective—big shocker here!—while you're reading your text chapters. Here you'll first encounter several dozen key terms from the chapter; I would recommend that you know these words "big time" (as Vice President Cheney famously once said). You'll also find a medley of exercises and questions. You should *not* be using these questions as a final test of your knowledge for that chapter. These exercises were designed so that you could complete them as you go along with your readings. In other words, they're meant to reinforce and solidify your understanding of what you've just read. *Be advised that you will not find the answers to these exercises contained in this study guide.* In case you're wondering, "What gives here?"—this decision was done because the purpose of these exercises are for *you* to search for the responses. By doing this, you'll be actively engaged with the material, so, when test time comes around, you should know this material quite well. In this section, you'll also find a thought-provoking question where you're asked to relate the chapter material to thinking about the September eleventh disaster and its aftermath. I think you'll get a lot out of these questions intellectually and personally.

OK, you wanted practice tests? No problem! Check out the "After you read" section for four exams. The first three exams contain ten multiple-choice questions. Each of these three practice tests covers a subset of the chapter. When you're done with these, complete the comprehensive exam: This twenty-three item (fifteen multiple choice, eight true-false) exam covers material from the entire chapter. Whether you choose to complete all four exams at once or take them one at a time is up to you, of course. However, I'd probably recommended the latter suggestion.

We're not done yet…we still have the "When you have finished section." There are two basic elements to this last section. For each chapter, you'll find a "Top Five List" suggesting how the material contained in each respective chapter is relevant for *your* life. I also suggest some interesting exercises that you might consider doing either for a class project or for your own personal enjoyment. After reading these sections, I hope you'll share not only my passion for social psychology but also my strong belief that it is relevant for *all* of our lives. Also, in this section, you'll find five short-answer/essay questions. Obviously, these questions are meant to further solidify your understanding of the material by forcing you to think about the chapter on a deeper level. The answers to all of these short answer/essay questions, as well as the questions contained in the "After you read" section, can be found in an appendix at the end of this study guide.

One more thing to note, if you still need MORE questions and exercises, check out the Web site for this text www.ablongman.com/baronbyrne. I think you'll find it to be another valuable resource too.

I wish you well in your studies and I sincerely hope that this study aid will be of help to you.

Eric D. Miller, Ph.D.
Assistant Professor of Psychology
Kent State University, East Liverpool Campus

1 THE FIELD OF SOCIAL PSYCHOLOGY: HOW WE THINK ABOUT AND INTERACT WITH OTHERS

Before you read . . .

This chapter introduces you to the field of social psychology, which is the scientific study of the nature and causes of individual behavior and thought in social situations. You will have a thorough overview of the type of issues that are studied by social psychologists and you'll be given an explanation of why social psychology is considered a science. Afterward, you'll have a good understanding of the general types of factors and variables that can influence social thought and behavior. You should also be on the lookout for an interesting discussion of some of the hottest contemporary trends in social psychology research. Following that, you'll have a very detailed exposure to the methods of social psychology research; here some of the mystery and intrigue that surrounds such studies will be explained. As part of this discussion, particular emphasis will be placed on a comparison of correlational and experimental studies. After a brief and user-friendly overview of the role of statistics and theories in social psychology research, the chapters concludes with a discussion of the importance of ethics when conducting social psychology research.

Chapter Objectives

After reading this chapter, you should be able to:

- Offer a definition of social psychology and discuss the types of issues this field considers.

- State the four key components to a science.

- Consider how social psychology differs from the field of sociology.

- State and briefly discuss the five major headings that characterize the variables of interest to most social psychologists.

- Discuss some of the major contemporary research trends in social psychology.

- Consider the advantages and limitations to systematic observations and the survey method.

- Describe the correlational method including the meaning of correlational coefficients and the key drawback to this method.

- Outline the nature of the experimental method, including all of the key components to this methodology.

- Explain the basic purpose of inferential statistics and meta-analysis.

- Define the term, "theory," and describe the procedure involved in building theories.

- Consider when and how deception is used in social psychological research.

- Discuss the importance of informed consent and debriefing in social psychological research.

As you read . . .

> **Remember this!** Below are a list of some of the key terms and concepts from this chapter. **Make flashcards in order to enhance your recall ability of these terms.** Refer to the definitions that are either in boldface or in the margins of this chapter for help. Be advised that you may also want to include additional terms from this chapter as you deem necessary.

Social psychology	Accuracy	Objectivity
Skepticism	Open-mindedness	Sociology
Cognitive processes	Evolutionary psychology	Variation
Inheritance	Selection	Heuristic vs. Systematic
Multicultural perspective	Systematic/Naturalistic observation	Survey method
Sampling	Correlational method	Hypothesis
Experimental method	Independent variable	Dependent variable
Random assignment	Experimenter effects	Double-blind procedure
External validity	Inferential statistics	Statistically significant
Meta-analysis	Theories	Deception
Informed consent	Debriefing	

Social Psychology: A Working Definition

➤ Social Psychology Is Scientific Nature

1. In your own words, offer a definition of social psychology.

2. Listed below are a variety of research questions. Place a star next to the ones that appear to have definite relevance to the field of social psychology.

   _____   Why does schizophrenia develop?

   _____   How do people fall in love?

   _____   How do children acquire the ability to comprehend language?

   _____   Under what conditions might we comply with a request from a person?

   _____   Have gender stereotypes changed over the past few decades?

   _____   When people help others, do they expect some sort of reward in return?

3. Calling all debaters! Listed below are a few points that a person could make about the nature of science. Your job is to offer a "counterpart" that refutes the point made.

   Point: *Science simply refers to fields like biology, chemistry, and physics.*

   Counterpoint:

   Point: *Science doesn't really have core values.*

   Counterpoint:

   Point: *Social psychology is nothing but good old-fashioned common sense.*

   Counterpoint:

➤ Social Psychology Focus on the Behavior of Individuals

1. Explain how and why sociology is different from social psychology.

➤ Social Psychology Seeks to Understand the Causes of Social Behavior and Thought

1. Listed below are a variety of variables that can influence social behavior and thought. Place these variables under the correct heading in the chart below.

memories of past behavior

behaviors toward elderly vs. young people

the appropriateness of giving gifts to college professors

passing genetic variations onto future generations

how we act when the weather is hot

what is considered by most to be "sexy"

whether we are more helpful when exposed to a pleasant smell

the role of construals

The Actions and Characteristics of Other Persons	Cognitive Processes	Environmental Variables	Cultural Context	Biological Factors

2. *Let it flow!* Complete this flowchart that summarizes the process of evolution by inserting and defining the appropriate terms—selection, inheritance, and variation—below.

> ## Social Psychology: Summing Up

1. Social behavior and thought are influenced by a wide range of _____,

_____, _____, _____, and _____

factors.

Social Psychology in the New Millennium: New Perspectives, New Methods

> ## Influence of a Cognitive Perspective

1. State the two *most* important ways that the cognitive perspective is reflected in social psychological research.

➤ Growing Emphasis on Application: Exporting Social Psychology

1. State three or four areas that illustrate how social psychology has been applied.

2. What did Kurt Lewin mean when he said, "There's nothing as practical as a good theory?"

➤ Adoption of a Multicultural Perspective: Taking Full Account of Social Diversity

1. Define what is meant by a "multicultural perspective." Why wasn't such a perspective largely adopted until fairly recently by social psychologists? To put it another way, how did most social psychologists address and conceptualize the issue of diversity in the 1960s and 1970s?

> ## Increasing Attention to the Potential Role of Biological Factors and the Evolutionary Perspective

1. Look at the picture of the man below and compare it with the men pictured on page 17. Which of these two men does the male figure below resemble? Given your response, what predictions might evolutionary psychology make for the male pictured below?

Answering Questions about Social Behavior and Social Thought: Research Methods in Social Psychology

> ## Systematic Observation: Describing the World around Us

1. Systematic observation involves _____

_____.

2. Define what is meant by a naturalistic observation and denote how such an investigation occurs.

3. Identify the advantages of the survey method and note the two main issues that *must* be carefully addressed when undertaking such a method.

➤ Correlation: The Search for Relationships

1. Underline the words in the parentheses that will make the following statement correct:

The term, correlation, refers to a tendency for one event to (cause another event, change as the other changes). When a correlation exists, it is possible to (predict, explain) one variable from information about one or more variables. So, the correlational method tells us (whether only, whether and to what extent) two variables are related to each other. Correlations can range from (0 to 100, 0 to –1.00 or 0 to +1.00), whereby the (greater, less) departure from 0, the stronger the correlation. (Positive, negative) numbers mean that as one variable increases, the other variable increases; (positive, negative) numbers show that as one variable increases, the other decreases.

2. Rank it! Rank order the following correlation coefficient values such that a "1" indicates the strongest correlation and a "5" indicates the weakest.

_____ +.49 _____ -.63 _____ +.17 _____ -.81 _____ +.33

3. Suppose a researcher finds that the average amount of time that a person exercises per week and the number of sweets they have per week is -.72. Briefly state what this correlation tells us about the relationship between these two variables.

➤ The Experimental Method: Knowledge through Systematic Intervention

1. Match it! Match each phrase, word, or sentence on the left side of the page with an identifying concept on the right side of the page. Note that each item on the right should be used *only once*.

__1. Situations where researchers aren't informed of a study's hypothesis.	A. experimentation
__2. The extent to which findings generalize to real life.	B. independent variable
__3. Allowing for an equal chance of exposure to each of the levels in the study.	C. dependent variable
__4. The variable that's measured.	D. random assignment
__5. A method that allows for understanding causality.	E. experimenter effects
__6. Unintended effects on subjects' behavior caused by researchers.	F. double-blind procedure
__7. The variable that's systematically varied.	G. external validity

2. Suppose Professor Green randomly assigns research participants to one of the following conditions: They are instructed to ride an exercise bike for either zero, fifteen, or thirty minutes. Afterward, she asks subjects to rate their positive mood.

   a.) What is the independent variable?

   b.) What is the dependent variable?

   c.) How many levels does this experimental study have?

➤ Interpreting Research Results: The Use of Statistics and Social Psychologists as Perennial Skeptics

1. What are inferential statistics and why do social psychologists use them?

2. What is a meta-analysis and why do social psychologists use this technique?

3. *On the road again....* It definitely is a long road from the moment a theory is tested to when it ultimately is decided as to whether the confidence in the theory will be increased or decreased. In the chart below, outline the steps needed in order for us to make a judgment as to whether the confidence in the theory will increase or decrease.

Confidence in the theory is INCREASED	Confidence in the theory is REDUCED

The Quest for Knowledge and Rights of Individuals: Seeking an Appropriate Balance

1. Why is deception sometimes used in social psychological research? How do social psychologists try to safeguard against any adverse effects when using it? What do research participants tend to think about its use in research?

Thinking about The Aftermath of the September 11, 2001 Attacks and Social Psychology

Arguably, we are all living through the biggest event of our lives—and one of the most historical events in American history—from the moment that first hijacked plane hit the Twin Towers. In an attempt to apply and further our understanding of these tragic and momentous series of events—and how they relate to various facets of social psychology—you will find a "thought question" where you will have to carefully integrate and analyze the material explored in this and all of the subsequent chapters. It is further hoped that these questions allow for some personal reflection about these historical events as well.

Identify and discuss issues and topics pertaining to the September eleventh tragedy that you think social psychologists need to research in the years ahead. Try to outline at least one experimental or correlational study that *you* would like to conduct regarding one of these issues if you had the opportunity to do so.

After you read . . . Practice Tests

Practice Test 1

1. A scientific field is different from a non-scientific field in terms of
   a. the applied nature of the issues that are studied.
   b. the values and methods that are adopted and used.
   c. whether the investigators hold advanced degrees
   d. whether a physical or social phenomenon is studied.

2. Representative sampling and wording of questions are particularly important when conducting a(n)
   a. survey.
   b. correlational study.
   c. experiment.
   d. naturalistic observation.

3. All of the following represent current trends in social psychology, *except*
   a. continued growth in the influence of the cognitive perspective.
   b. increased interest in studying diversity and the impact of cultural factors on social behavior.
   c. an increasing importance in applying the principles and findings of social psychology.
   d. decreased emphasis on the necessity for informed consent and debriefing.

4. An experimenter exposed subjects to systematically varied levels of temperature to determine its effect on aggression. The temperature level is the _____ variable.
   a. independent
   b. dependent
   c. control
   d. theoretical

5. When the results of an experiment can be generalized to real-life social situations, the experiment has
   a. external validity.
   b. statistical significance.
   c. theoretical relevance.
   d. random assignment.

6. A sophisticated statistical technique for combing results from many experiments in order to reach an overall conclusion regarding the topic in question is called
   a. replication.
   b. a correlational coefficient.
   c. meta-analysis.
   d. converging operations.

7. A primary goal of social psychological theories is to provide
   a. a description of social behavior.
   b. an explanation of social behavior.
   c. ethical guidelines for researchers.
   d. a summary of previous research in social psychology.

8. A key reason why a social psychologist may use deception in a study is to
   a. protect subjects from the harmful effects of learning negative aspects about themselves.
   b. illustrate that causal relationships between independent and dependent variables cannot be established without the use of deception.
   c. simply obtain useful knowledge that otherwise might not be possible if subjects knew the true purpose of the study.
   d. satisfy the wishes of research participants who routinely enjoy experiments where deception is involved.

9. A research participant gives their _____ once they are told about what a particular study will involve. Once the study is completed, the research participant is given a(n) _____, or a full description about the nature of the research
   a. deceptive cues; debriefing
   b. safeguarding; informed consent
   c. debriefing; informed consent
   d. informed consent; debriefing

10. The reaction of most research participants to temporary deception appears to be
    a. overwhelmingly negative.
    b. a feeling of concern followed by intrigue.
    c. not negative provided that its purpose and necessity are clear.
    d. overwhelmingly positive.

Practice Test 2

1. The scientific field that seeks to understand the nature and causes of individual behavior and thought in social situations is called
   a. social science.
   b. social psychology.
   c. sociology.
   d. personality psychology.

2. Research involving whether people react differently to the elderly than younger persons primarily involves the study of variables pertaining to
   a. the actions and characteristics of other people.
   b. cognitive processes.
   c. the cultural context.
   d. environmental variables.

3. Biological processes and genetic factors
   a. are unrelated to social behavior.
   b. completely predict social behavior.
   c. affect social behavior to some extent.
   d. might influence social behavior but this issue hasn't been studied yet.

4. The cognitive perspective reflects basic knowledge about all of the following areas, *except*
   a. memory.
   b. psychopathology.
   c. reasoning.
   d. decision making.

5. Kurt Lewin once offered this famous quote: "There's nothing as practical as a good ____."
   a. idea
   b. research study
   c. social psychologist
   d. theory

6. A research technique that is often included under the heading of systematic observation is the ____ method.
   a. correlational
   b. survey
   c. experimental
   d. meta-analysis

7. Which of the following correlation coefficients is impossible to have?
   a. -1
   b. 1
   c. 0
   d. 10

8. A(n) ____ based on a theory is the definition of a hypothesis.
   a. unverified prediction
   b. verified prediction
   c. unverified statement of fact
   d. verified statement of fact

9. When two variables are correlated, we can assume that there is a causal link between these
   a. only if the result is statistically significant.
   b. only when the correlation coefficient value is close to −1 or +1.
   c. under no conditions.
   d. under any conditions.

10. Professor Green and Professor White are conducting research studies in social psychology. Professor Green wants to randomly assign subjects to his two conditions by alternating order (e.g., the first subject goes in the first condition, the second subject goes in the second condition, the third subject goes in the first condition, etc.) whereas Professor White wants to randomly assign subjects on the basis of their sex (e.g., men go in the first condition and women go in the second condition). Which of the following statements *best* summarizes whether random assignment has been followed?
   a. Both professors have randomly assigned their subjects.
   b. Neither professor has randomly assigned their subjects.
   c. Professor Green has randomly assigned his subjects, but Professor White has not.
   d. Professor White has randomly assigned his subjects, but Professor Green has not.

Practice Test 3

1. Experimenter effects can often be avoided if _____ is used.
   a. double-blind procedure
   b. random assignment
   c. external validity
   d. the correlational method

2. A research result is considered to be "significant" when
   a. a majority of social psychologists claim it to be so.
   b. it has applied relevance.
   c. the likelihood of obtaining the observed findings by chance is low.
   d. the result appears to be important in some way.

3. Suppose a theory supported by Dr. Williams has ultimately been accepted. What are the implications of this decision?
   a. No further research on this theory is necessary.
   b. The theory still remains open to further refinement.
   c. Outside reviews should question whether Dr. Williams' decision was ethical.
   d. We can assume that Dr. Williams noted many instances where his results were inconsistent with the theory.

4. Right before Professor Peterson is about to begin her study, she tells her research participants that they will be sampling a variety of cookies. This is consistent with
   a. truth-telling.
   b. informed consent.
   c. deception.
   d. debriefing.

5. The view that social psychology should apply to all humans regardless of where they live or their cultural identity is
   a. generally considered to be racist.
   b. consistent with the multicultural perspective.
   c. no longer dominant within the field.
   d. fairly accurate and accepted by most social psychologists.

6. During a naturalistic observation, the experimenter
   a. tries to ask prospective research participants as many questions as possible.
   b. absolutely must make use of random assignment.
   c. should be very concerned about the wording of questions used during the study.
   d. attempts to avoid influencing the persons observed.

7. Which of the following correlation coefficient orders represent values ranging from the weakest to the strongest?
   a. -.66; 0; +.33
   b. +.54; -.61; -.49
   c. -.80; -.22; 0
   d. +.18; -.27; -.41

8. When an independent variable is confounded with another variable,
   a. the results of an experiment may be meaningless.
   b. this suggests that the experimenter failed to use random assignment.
   c. we can assume that the experiment is a success since this should occur in an experimental study.
   d. this offers evidence that we should reject the given theory.

9. Meta-analysis is considered to be a(n) _____ procedure.
   a. correlational
   b. experimental
   c. mathematical
   d. theoretical

10. Suppose you learn that a certain researcher has claimed to have "proven a theory of social behavior." How should you respond to the researcher's statement?
    a. You should ask the researcher to explain the methods of his or her study.
    b. You should ask the researcher to state how he or she has proven the theory.
    c. You should tell the researcher that we can never prove a theory in any absolute way.
    d. You should congratulate the researcher on proving the theory, given how difficult it is to "prove" any theory.

Comprehensive Test
(NOTE: Items 1-15 are multiple-choice questions and items 16-23 are true-false questions.)

1. Which of the following is considered to be a component of the definition of social psychology?
   a. It is a science.
   b. It focuses on large groups of persons.
   c. It is used to understand the nature of social situations only.
   d. It primarily examines individual behavior.

2. When Dr. Williamson discovers that a certain result hasn't been replicated in a study, she grows wary of initial claims made by a certain researcher. This example *best* illustrates the importance of _____ in scientific research.
   a. accuracy
   b. objectivity
   c. skepticism
   d. open-mindedness

3. The fact that many people believe that "opposites attract" and "birds of a feather flock together" suggests that
   a. the scientific method has very limited applications.
   b. most people have a good understanding of human behavior irrespective of whether they are psychologists.
   c. common sense often portrays a confusing, inconsistent picture of human behavior.
   d. it is very difficult to even begin to understand the dynamics of interpersonal attraction.

4. All of the following issues would be illustrative of environmental variables, *except*
   a. whether we act more aggressive when it is hot.
   b. whether we are more likely to help others after smelling a pleasant odor.
   c. what is considered to be attractive in a given country or culture.
   d. the impact of a full moon on social behavior.

5. The crucial, concrete outcome of evolution is _____.
   a. variation
   b. inheritance
   c. selection
   d. attraction

6. Which of the following is *not* a current trend in social psychology?
   a. An increased emphasis on cognitive processes by ignoring the relevance of social behavior.
   b. An increased importance of applying social psychological research to other fields.
   c. The adoption of a multicultural perspective.
   d. A general acknowledgment of the importance of biological and genetic factors in social behavior.

7. The issue of sampling in survey research suggests the importance of
    a. random assignment.
    b. systematic manipulation of a certain variable.
    c. making sure the researcher isn't noticed by the research participants.
    d. having participants who are representative of the larger population.

8. A correlation coefficient value of ____ is greater than a correlation coefficient value of ____.
    a. +.80; -.90
    b. -.31; +.21
    c. 0; -.52
    d. +.44; -.44

9. The greatest flaw of a correlational study is generally considered to be its inability to
    a. be used in natural settings.
    b. gather a large amount of information in a short period of time.
    c. highly efficient.
    d. draw conclusive causal relationships.

10. Suppose Dr. Kern devises an experimental study where her research participants either watch zero, five, or fifteen minutes of very violent television and then she takes their pulse. In this study, there would be ____ levels of the independent variable.
    a. two
    b. three
    c. four
    d. twenty

11. Unintended effects on participants' behavior produced by researchers are known as
    a. deceptive acts.
    b. experimenter effects.
    c. double-blind procedures.
    d. external validity effects.

12. A key reason why social psychological research often yields inconsistent findings is due to
    a. a poor understanding of statistical methods used in research.
    b. the fact that social psychology can never explain human behavior "across the board."
    c. the use of different methods by different researchers.
    d. a general dependence on outdated theories of social thought and behavior.

13. For the confidence in a theory to be reduced,
    a. its predictions must have been disconfirmed.
    b. the theory must be rejected.
    c. the research designed to test its predictions must be faulty.
    d. the theory must be worthless.

14. The use of deception in social psychological research
    a. is no longer permitted.
    b. usually causes great harm to those exposed to it.
    c. is typically not tolerated by research participants.
    d. must never be used to persuade people to participate in a study.

15. All of the following are guiding principles for researchers in social psychology, *except*
    a. use deception only when it is absolutely essential to do so.
    b. always proceed with caution.
    c. make certain that all possible precautions are taken to safeguard the protection and well-being of subjects.
    d. try to avoid telling the research participant about the true nature of the study once they have completed it.

16. Your text asserts that highly advanced fields, such as physics, chemistry, and biology, are scientific in nature, whereas social psychology does *not* meet the criteria of being a "science."

17. Our judgments about persons we meet are likely to be influenced by the mood we are in when we meet them.

18. Social psychology focuses its study on groups of persons or society as a whole.

19. The role of construals in determining social behavior is primarily studied by evolutionary social psychologists.

20. Strong findings in correlational studies provide conclusive evidence that the variables being measured have a causal relationship with each other.

21. The preferred method of research by social psychologists has generally been the experimental method.

22. The goal of social psychological research is to prove that a particular theory of social behavior is true.

23. Social psychologists typically believe that it is permissible to use deception without informed consent and debriefing.

When You Have Finished . . .

TOP TEN REASONS WHY THE STUDY OF SOCIAL PSYCHOLOGY HAS GREAT RELEVANCE FOR *YOUR* LIFE

At this point, perhaps you may be thinking, "OK, this stuff is interesting, but what does it have to do with *my* life?" That's certainly a very fair question. Remember that social psychologists typically try to apply many of their theories and empirical findings to "real" people in the "real" world—lest we forget Kurt

Lewin's (the "founding father" of social psychology) famous maxim, "There's nothing as practical as a good theory." Let us try to specifically list how the study of social psychology truly has meaningful relevance for our lives on an everyday basis. Even though David Letterman will probably never offer this list on his show, consider the following "Top Five List" detailing why social psychology has great relevance for *your* life:

1. Since we all truly are 'social animals' who are interacting with others on a regular basis, *life itself* represents a study of social psychology!

2. We are consumers of information. By understanding scientific methods and what is considered to be "scientific," we are better equipped to carefully and critically analyze such information.

3. If we are aware of all of the possible major factors that influence social thought and behavior, then we will be more apt to pinpoint the possible causes of these thoughts or behaviors.

4. Since many social psychologists are concerned with applying their research findings in order to better the lives of people in the "real world," in some way you may have already benefited from the work of social psychologists (perhaps without even knowing it)!

5. If *you* are considering a career in psychology or other scientific fields, understanding the basic dynamics of research methodology will help further your career.

For each of the following chapters, you will be presented with different "Top Five Lists." Be advised that this (and the other) "Top Five Lists" represents the (Study Guide) author's subjective view as to how these items should be ranked. A fun exercise might be for *you* to come up with your own "Top Five List" for each of the chapters. Additionally, I would encourage you—whether it be for paper assignments, class presentations, or general personal enrichment—to try to extend any or all of these points (from each of these lists) into a related exercise or project. To this end, I will suggest some possible exercises. For instance, with respect to point #5, design an experimental and/or correlational study examining some area of interest to you in social psychology. After you've outlined your design and questions, ask a few of your friends or family members to complete your "study" just for fun. Try to get a sense for whether your predictions were validated from your findings. Above all, be creative and have fun doing these exercises!

Short Answer/Essay Questions

1. **Social Psychology as a Science**
   State the four most important core values to a scientific field.

2. **Biological Factors of Social Behavior**
   State and briefly define the three basic components of evolution.

3. **Correlational Studies**
   Suppose Professor Stone conducts a correlational study in which he asks individuals how many times (on average) they get into an argument with a friend or close other and the number of colds (on average) they get per year. If he records a correlation coefficient value of -.43, what does this value specifically tell us about the relationship between these two variables?

4. **Experimental Studies**
   Suppose Dr. Wheeler conducts an experimental study in which research participants who are in a romantic relationship are asked to write about the benefits of their relationships, the drawbacks to the relationships, or to write about what they ate for breakfast that morning. Then, she measures and records each of the subject's blood pressure. Identify the independent and dependent variables in this study.

5. **The Role of Deception in Social Psychology Research**
   Provide a brief overview of why deception is sometimes used in social psychological research, the problems that can result after using it, and how to minimize such problems.

2 SOCIAL PERCEPTION:
UNDERSTANDING OTHERS

Before you read . . .

This chapter introduces you to the study of social perception, which is a series of processes that attempt to understand other persons. You will first consider why nonverbal communication allows us to express our own and interpret others' emotions, attitudes, and feelings. You will also read about how you may determine whether a person is lying based on their nonverbal cues. Afterward, you will be looking at how we attempt to understand the causes of our own and others' behavior through the study of attributions. As part of this discussion, you will discover how and why our attributions are often incorrect and how these are often applied in the "real world." Following that, you'll learn about the functions of impression formation and impression management. You will learn about a very well-known study by a famous social psychologist, Solomon Asch, which considers how we combine and use social information. The many ways by which we try to look good to others will also be reviewed. This chapter concludes with a consideration of whether social perception truly allows us to gather accurate information.

Chapter Objectives

After reading this chapter, you should be able to:

- Describe the major purpose and functions of social perception.

- Define what is meant by nonverbal communication and how it is related to the concepts and terms, "irrepressible," "deception," and "emotional contagion."

- Describe the six (or perhaps seven) basic emotions expressed in unique facial expressions. Does this mean we are limited to only a small number of facial expressions?

- Describe how body language, including gestures, posture, and movements, can communicate emotion, including such examples as ballet and various emblems.

- Identify and describe the five key nonverbal cues that may allow us to recognize deception.

- Compare and contrast the key elements of Jones and Davis' theory of correspondent inference with Kelley's theory of attribution.

- Explain the difference between internal and external causes and controllable versus uncontrollable factors.

- Contrast the discounting and augmenting principles.

- Describe and contrast the major attributional errors: the correspondence bias, the actor-observer effect, and the self-serving bias. Consider cultural differences with respect to these biases.

- Discuss how attribution theory has been applied to the study of depression and prejudice.

- Discuss how Asch's research on central and peripheral traits support his view that forming impressions involves more than simply adding together individual traits.

- Contrast older models of how we combine diverse information about others into unified impressions of them with more contemporary perspectives.

- Describe the role played by exemplars and abstractions when we make judgments about others.

- List self-enhancement tactics and other-enhancement tactics used in impression management, and describe research results on whether these tactics "pay off" for persons using them.

- Provide evidence to support the idea that we are quite accurate in social perception.

As you read . . .

> Remember this! Below are a list of some of the key terms and concepts from this chapter. Make flashcards in order to enhance your recall ability of these terms. Refer to the definitions that are either in boldface or in the margins of this chapter for help. Be advised that you may also want to include additional terms from this chapter as you deem necessary.

Social perception	Nonverbal behavior	Irrepressible
Emotional contagion	Basic channels	The "basic" emotions
Gazes and stares	Microexpressions/deception	Body language
Correspondent inference theory	Attribution	Noncommon effects
Theory of causal attributions	Social desirability	Internal/external causes
Consensus	Consistency	Distinctiveness
Stable vs. controllable factors	Discounting	Augmenting
Regulatory focus theory	Promotion vs. prevention focus	Reasons
Causal history of reason	Fundamental attribution error	Correspondence bias
Salient/Perceptual salience	Individualistic vs. collectivistic culture	Attributions and prejudice/depression
Self-serving bias	Actor-observer effect	Gestalt psychology
Central/peripheral traits	Impression formation	Negativity effect

SOCIAL PERCEPTION

Exemplars	Abstractions	Categorical judgments
Impression management	Self-enhancement tactics	Other-enhancement tactics
Slime effect	Cognitive load	

Nonverbal Communication: The Language of Expressions, Gazes, and Gestures

➤ Nonverbal Communication: The Basic Channels

1. Complete the following statement by filling in the blanks:

    We pay careful attention to _____ provided by changes in people's facial

    expressions, eye contact, posture, body movements, and other expressive actions. These behaviors

    are often called _____ because these are difficult to control.

2. Name that number! How many "basic channels" of communication are there?

3. Listed below are several common emotions. Circle the six basic emotions that are represented clearly
    on the human face and from a very early age. Underline the other emotion that is thought to be quite
    basic.

happiness	surprise
love	anger
contempt	desire
jealousy	fear
disgust	relief
anger	sadness
disappointment	worry

4. "The *eyes* have it!" Give at least one example of how eye contact may suggest that a person likes us and at least one example of how eye contact may indicate that a person dislikes us.

5. Name that emotion! For each of the following expressions, state the emotion that is likely being conveyed:

   a. Large number of movements where one part of the body does something to another part:
   _____

   b. Rounded postures: _____

   c. Firm handshakes: _____

➤ Recognizing Deception: The Role of Nonverbal Cues

1. *"I cannot tell a lie…"* Just in case you're wondering whether someone really did cut down a cherry tree—or are being truthful about a more serious matter—you may want to pay attention to their nonverbal cues. Listed below are five nonverbal expressions. Determine whether the expressions below would indicate whether the person is telling a lie or being honest:

   a. Seeing one facial expression quickly followed by another: _____

   b. Observing a person who manages their facial expressions well but cannot look you in the eye as he or she talks to you: _____

   c. Observing a person who is speaking very clearly and whose pitch of voice does not rise:
   _____

   d. Observing an individual who has very dilated pupils: _____

   e. Showing very exaggerated facial expressions: _____

2. Underline the words in the parentheses that will make each of the following two statements correct:

   a.) When we are trying to determine if someone is deceiving us, we tend to pay more attention to their

   (words, nonverbal cues) because we have (unlimited, limited) cognitive capacity. As result of this,

   we tend to be (more, less) effective at detecting deception.

25

b.) People tend to be (more, less, just as) accurate at recognizing lies within their own cultures than another culture. Overall, people tend to be fairly (good, poor) at recognizing lies told by persons from a different culture.

> ## Beyond The Headlines: As Social Psychologists See It…Fragrance: A Fading Nonverbal Cue?

1. How might fragrance act as a nonverbal cue? Can you think of any personal instances in your own life when a fragrance function as a nonverbal cue?

Attribution: Understanding the Causes of Others' Behavior

> ## Theories of Attribution: Frameworks for Understanding How We Attempt to Make Sense of the Social World

1. a. Jones and Davis' (1965) theory of _____ asks how we use information about

   others' behavior as a basis for inferring that they possess various traits.

   b. List the three factors that will typically lead us to conclude that others' behavior reflects their stable traits:

2. Let's make a...chart! Listed below is an incomplete chart that details the three main components of Kelley's theory of causal attributions. Your job is to complete the chart by: (a) defining the three terms and (b) on the basis of the information given, determine whether we would ultimately make an internal or external attribution regarding the hypothetical cause.

Component	Definition	High or Low?	Internal or External Cause?
Consensus		Low	
Distinctiveness		Low	
Consistency		High	

Suppose consensus, distinctiveness, and consistency were *all high*. Would we attribute behavior in this case to internal or external causes?

3. Match it! Match each phrase, word, or sentence on the left side of the page with an identifying concept on the right side of the page. Note that each item on the right should be used *only once*.

____1. Whether an individual can change behavior if they want to.   A. reasons

____2. Viewing the first possible cause as less likely due to other causes.   B. promotion focus

____3. Adding weight to a factor when we aren't expecting it to to make a difference.   C. augmenting

____4. Emphasizing the presence and absence of positive outcomes.   D. controllable factors

____5. Emphasizing negative outcomes.   E. prevention focus

____6. Conscious desires, values, or beliefs.   F. causal history of reason

____7. Factors that shape behavior in a way that the persons involved are unaware of.   G. discounting

SOCIAL PERCEPTION

➤ Attribution: Some Basic Sources of Error

1. Indicate whether the following three statements about the correspondence bias are true or false:

   a.) The correspondence bias is a tendency to explain other's actions as stemming from situational causes and not their dispositions.

   b.) The correspondence bias is often referred to as the fundamental attribution error.

   c.) The correspondence bias is more common in collectivistic cultures than individualistic cultures.

2. According to the actor-observer effect, when you fail at something you will likely attribute it to

   _____ causes. However, if one of your classmates fails at something, you will likely

   attribute this to _____ causes. When we succeed at something though, we tend to

   attribute it to internal causes. This is known as the _____.

➤ Applications of Attribution Theory: Insights and Interventions

1. Define it!

   a.) What are self-defeating attributions? Who are the individuals most likely to express these patterns of attributions?

   b.) What does it mean to be labeled as a "chronic complainer?"

28

Impression Formation and Impression Management: How We Combine and Use Social Information

➢ **Asch's Research on Central and Peripheral Traits**

1. Solomon Asch was greatly influenced by the work of _____ psychologists.

2. In one of Asch's famous studies on impression formation, he showed his research participants two lists of words. Name the two words that were classified as "central traits."

➢ **Impression Formation: A Cognitive Perspective**

1. The study of impression formation examines _____

_____.

➢ **Social Psychology: Thirty Years of Progress…From Cognitive Algebra to Motivated Processing**

1. Compare and contrast how social psychologists believed we combined diverse information about others into unified impressions of them thirty years ago (Then) versus the more current views on this topic (Now).

        Then   Now

2. The _____ illustrates that we tend to pay more attention to negative than positive

information about others.

➤ Other Aspects of Impression Formation: The Nature of First Impressions and Our Motives for Forming Them

1. Exemplar or Abstraction?: You Be The Judge! State whether the following events are exemplars or abstractions:

Event	Exemplar or Abstraction?
Our first impression of someone.	
Our belief about someone's personality solely on the basis of his or her profession.	
Our belief that a person is kind on the basis of previous interactions.	
Our impression of a co-worker that we've known for many years.	

➤ Impression Management: The Fine Art of Looking Good

1. The study of impression management examines _____

_____.

2. *You look (or you make me look) marvelous!* Listed in the table below are a variety of impression management techniques. Complete the table by stating for each technique: a.) whether it is a self-enhancement or an other-enhancement tactic, and b) whether it is likely to be successful.

Tactic	Self-enhancement or other-enhancement?	Will it be successful?
Describing oneself in positive terms.		
Boosting one's physical appearance.		
Offering excessively flattering statements.		
Showing a high degree of interest in another person.		
Exhibiting behavior that is characterized as "licking upward but kicking downward."		

3. For each of the following three hypothetical individuals, state whether cognitive load would likely increase or decrease their abilities to present themselves favorably.

Individual	Increase or decrease?
A professor interviewing for a job at a university.	
A person on a first date who is trying to find the way to a new restaurant.	
An introvert who is trying to act like an extravert while performing another task.	

> ## The Accuracy of Social Perception: Evidence That It's Higher Than You May Think

1. State at least one reason why social psychologists believe that we are quite successful about our ability to form accurate perceptions of others even if we have very little information to go by.

Thinking about The Aftermath of the September 11, 2001 Attacks and Social Perception

When people first heard about the September eleventh attacks, many individuals were overcome with various emotions. Reflecting back on September eleventh, do you recall any emotional expressions—either your own or others—that seemed "irrepressible?" Explain your response. Also, try to recall the emotional states of others around you on that day. Did you witness or experience "emotional contagion?" If so, how?

After you read . . . Practice Tests

Practice Test 1

1. Facial expressions, eye contact, body movements, posture, and touching are the basic channels for
   a. nonverbal communication.
   b. attributions.
   c. impression management.
   d. impression formation.

2. Generally, we interpret a high level of (non-continuous) eye contact from another person as a sign of
   a. anger.
   b. disgust.
   c. liking.
   d. surprise.

3. Body movements that carry a specific meaning in a given culture are called
   a. irrepressible.
   b. emblems.
   c. emotional contagions.
   d. the six basic emotions.

4. ____ tend to have higher handshake index ratings than ____.
   a. Men; women
   b. Women; men
   c. Extraverts; introverts
   d. Introverts; Extraverts

5. A person who is trying to understand the causes behind someone's behavior is engaged in the process of
   a. deception.
   b. attribution.
   c. impression formation.
   d. staring.

6. According to Kelley's theory, the basic task we face in making a causal attribution is determining whether a behavior is caused by ____ or ____ causes.
   a. internal; external
   b. augmenting; discounting
   c. prevention; promotion
   d. noncommon; common

2. How many basic emotions are represented by a distinct facial expression?
   a. none
   b. only one
   c. six or seven
   d. the number is limitless

3. A high level of eye contact is usually interpreted as a sign of ____, avoiding eye contact as a sign of ____, and staring as a sign of ____.
   a. friendliness; unfriendliness; hostility
   b. unfriendliness; friendliness; hostility
   c. friendliness; hostility; unfriendliness
   d. hostility; friendliness; unfriendliness

4. Aronoff, Woike, and Hyman (1992) studied body postures displayed in classical ballet and found that threatening postures were ____, while warm postures were ____.
   a. ambiguous; more easily defined
   b. easy to display; ambiguous
   c. rounded; angular
   d. angular; rounded

5. When we consciously are trying to detect deception, we tend to pay more attention to ____ cues which usually cause us to make ____ judgments as to whether the individual in question is lying.
   a. verbal; correct
   b. verbal; incorrect
   c. nonverbal; correct
   d. nonverbal; incorrect

6. The use of fragrance, which tends to be ____ nowadays, ____ a type of nonverbal cue.
   a. increasing; is
   b. increasing; is not
   c. decreasing; is
   d. decreasing; is not

7. Assume your friend is marrying someone who has a single positive trait (he's very rich), but several negative traits. Apparently your friend is marrying this person for the money. This is an example of how ____ influence(s) our attributions.
   a. noncommon effects
   b. high social desirability
   c. low social desirability
   d. noncorrespondent inferences

8. We are likely to attribute another person's behavior to external causes when consensus is ____, consistency is ____, and distinctiveness is ____.
   a. high; high; high
   b. low; low; low
   c. low; high; low
   d. high; low; high

9. You are less likely to think a mother is mean-tempered if you learn she was shouting at her son because he just ran out in front of traffic. This illustrates
   a. the augmenting principle.
   b. the discounting principle.
   c. the fundamental attribution error.
   d. self-serving bias

10. Those with a _____ focus tend to be more interested in making _____, whereas those with a _____ focus tend to be more concerned about _____.
    a. promotion; hits; prevention; avoiding misses
    b. promotion; false alarms; prevention; hits
    c. prevention; hits; promotion; correct rejections
    d. promotion; hits; prevention; correct rejections

11. Complete the following analogy: Reasons is to aware as
    a. causal history of reason explanation is to unaware.
    b. desire is to belief.
    c. internal state is to causal history of reason explanation.
    d. thought is to behavior.

12. The correspondence bias refers to our tendency to
    a. explain others' actions in terms of traits.
    b. explain others' actions in terms of situations.
    c. give ourselves more credit for our own success than we really deserve.
    d. overestimate the role of situations in causing our own behavior.

13. The actor-observer effect suggests we perceive our own behavior stems largely from _____ causes, whereas we perceive the behavior of other persons stems largely from _____ causes.
    a. situational; internal
    b. internal; situational
    c. dispositional; internal
    d. external; situational

14. Depressives tend to show patterns of attributions _____ to those found with respect to _____.
    a. opposite; correspondence bias
    b. identical; self-serving bias
    c. opposite; self-serving bias
    d. identical; actor-observer effect

15. All of the following are examples of self-enhancement techniques of impression management, *except*
    a. wearing perfume.
    b. dressing in particular clothes.
    c. developing a suntan to improve personal appearance.
    d. directing flattering remarks to your target.

16. Emotional contagion is a mechanism through which feelings are automatically transferred from person to person.

17. Facial expressions are totally universal around the world.

18. A person is probably lying if his or her voice rises and he or she is making many speech errors.

19. We are likely to make a correspondence inference on the basis of behaviors that produce noncommon effects.

20. We are likely to attribute another person's behavior to external causes when consensus, consistency, and distinctiveness are all high.

21. Western European countries are usually characterized as collectivistic cultures.

22. Persons who are depressed tend to use the self-serving bias more than nondepressed persons.

23. At first, our impressions of others consist mainly of concrete behavioral exemplars, but after we have considerable experience with the person, our impressions are based mainly on mental abstractions.

When You Have Finished . . .

TOP TEN REASONS WHY SOCIAL PERCEPTION HAS GREAT RELEVANCE FOR *YOUR* LIFE

1. We are always trying to figure out other persons in terms of their motives, thinking, and their attitudes toward us. This is what social perception is all about!

2. We typically try to make the "best" impression—through impression management techniques--we can when we are interacting with others, particularly with respect to our initial encounters (such as job interviews, blind dates, etc.).

3. We are often in a position where we are trying to determine whether a person is being truthful to us; one of the best ways to determine this is by using nonverbal cues as a means of recognizing deception.

4. Whenever we are evaluating a person we have just met—particularly whether we "like" them—we tend to place great importance to various contextual and situational cues when describing their traits. Obviously this point suggests the relevance of Asch's classic research on central and peripheral traits.

5. Whenever we are trying to understand someone's actions, we ultimately try to ascertain whether it is due to the individual's unique characteristics or situational influences. We often use Jones and Davis' and Kelley's models of attributions on a regular basis (often without consciously realizing it!).

With respect to point #3, consider the following two possible exercises: (1) Interview five different friends of yours and ask them to tell you about a truthful incident and ask them to "make up" an incident. On the basis of their nonverbal reactions, see how well you can determine when they're lying or telling the truth; (2) A major news story in the summer of 2001 was the interview that U.S. Representative Gary

Condit had with news reporter Connie Chung regarding the Chandra Levy incident. Try to get a copy of that interview and determine for yourself, on the basis of nonverbal cues, whether Representative Condit is being truthful or not. Alternatively, view an interview of another public figure and consider whether that person is showing nonverbal signs of deception.

Short Answer/Essay Questions

1. **Nonverbal Behavior**
   Briefly state three factors that might allow us to determine whether a person is lying on the basis of his or her nonverbal behavior.

2. **Attributions**
   Imagine an individual in a theater talked very loudly throughout an entire movie. According to Jones and Davis' model, what would this information tell us about this person? Why?

3. **Applications of Attribution Theory**
   Suppose your friend, who is a minority, mentions to you that she thinks she has been the victim of racial discrimination at work and intends to inform her boss about this. Based on research pertaining to attribution and prejudice, what would you advise her to do?

4. **Impression Formation**
   What is the difference between an exemplar and an abstraction?

5. **Impression Management**
   Briefly state three factors that will usually foster other-enhancement.

3 SOCIAL COGNITION:
THINKING ABOUT THE SOCIAL WORLD

Before you read . . .

In this chapter, you'll be provided with an introduction to the study of social cognition; this field considers how we interpret, analyze, remember, and use information about the social world. After reading this chapter, you'll have a good understanding of why we often make many errors and mental short cuts when thinking about social information. In doing so, you'll be exposed to how heuristics and automatic processing operate. You'll also have a better appreciation for why total rationality in social cognition is not that common in light of such phenomena as the negativity and optimistic biases, counterfactual and magical thinking, and thought suppression. Despite all of these potential forms of cognitive bias, you'll also have an appreciation for why we still do a fairly good job of processing social information. The last segment of this chapter explores the two-way relationship between affect and cognition. In other words, as you can imagine, our feelings can influence our thoughts and our thoughts can influence our feelings.

Chapter Objectives

After reading this chapter, you should be able to:

- Discuss what is meant by "social cognition" and list the basic assumptions that most social psychologists have with respect to cognitive processes.

- State the basic purpose and function of schemas as well as the three basic processes that they influence.

- Consider how our schemas may (or may not) be altered in the face of new information.

- Discuss how the self-fulfilling prophecy may operate in certain applied settings, such as classroom environments.

- Explain why we often use heuristics and the consequences of their use. Contrast two different types of heuristics.

- Discuss the nature of automatic processing in social thought.

- Examine why we tend to show a negativity bias—particularly from an evolutionary or biological perspective.

- Consider the prevalence of the optimistic bias, its consequences, and when this bias typically is *not* shown.

- Understand why sometimes our tendency to do a minimal amount of cognitive work may be justified.

- Identify the effects that counterfactual thinking may have on our moods and general well-being.

- State the meaning of "magical thinking" as well as the three principles that pertain to this pattern of cognition.

- Explain what thought suppression is, why it can be—but often is *not*—effective, and identify the individual difference characteristic that is particularly susceptible to the negative effects of thought suppression.

- Provide a rationale for why we actually do a fairly good job in processing social information.

- Consider how affect can influence cognition by discussing mood-dependent memory, mood congruence effects, mental contamination, and the effects of being in a good mood on social behavior.

- List the three ways that cognition can influence affect.

As you read . . .

Remember this! Below are a list of some of the key terms and concepts from this chapter. Make flashcards in order to enhance your recall ability of these terms. Refer to the definitions that are either in boldface or in the margins of this chapter for help. Be advised that you may also want to include additional terms from this chapter as you deem necessary.

Social cognition	Affect	Schemas
Attention	Encoding	Retrieval
Perseverance effect	Self-fulfilling prophecy	Information overload
Heuristics	Representativeness heuristic	Availability heuristic
(Automatic) Priming	Automatic processing	Negativity bias
Optimistic bias	Planning fallacy	Brace for loss effect
Counterfactual thinking	Inaction inertia	Magical thinking
Laws of contagion/similarity	Thought suppression	Reactance
Mood-dependent memory	Mood congruence effect	Mental contamination
Two-factor theory of emotion		

Schemas: Mental Frameworks for Organizing and Using Social Information

➤ **The Impact of Schemas on Social Cognition: Attention, Encoding, Retrieval**

1. In your own words, what is meant by "social cognition?" Also, what are the two basic assumptions that most social psychologists tend to have about cognition?

2. Look at the picture below. It should activate a certain schema for you. Identify and describe that schema and, how your description further helps you to understand precisely what a schema is.

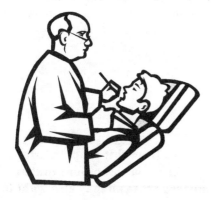

3. Schemas exert effects on three basic processes. State and define these three processes below.

        Process   Definition

4. What do we do with information that is inconsistent with our schemas? Is this information remembered better than information that is consistent with our schemas? How is the perseverance effect relevant to these two questions?

➤ Evidence for the Self-Confirming Nature of Schemas: When and Why Beliefs Shape Reality

1. Describe the nature of self-fulfilling prophecies by considering how this effect may operate in classroom situations.

2. Name the historical event that may have been caused, in part, due to the nature of self-fulfilling prophecies.

Heuristics and Automatic Processing: How We Reduce Our Effort in Social Cognition

➤ Representativeness: Judging by Resemblance

1. When do we experience information overload?

2. Why do we use heuristics?

3. Suppose Tom starts work at a new business and while setting up his office, he places a U.S. flag and a picture of U.S. President George W. Bush on his desk. Tom's co-workers are trying to "figure out" his personality—will they be more likely to say that he's "patriotic" or "patriotic and conservative" based on how the representativeness heuristic operates? Explain your response. Also, would such a judgment be accurate?

➤ Availability: "If I Can Think of It, It Must Be Important"

1. Even though, statistically, airplane flying is far safer than automobile driving many people claim a great fear of flying. How does the availability heuristic help to explain this apparent paradox?

2. How does priming help to explain the "medical student syndrome?"

> ## Automatic Processing in Social Thought: How We Manage to Do Two Things at Once

1. What is difference between automatic and controlled processing?

2. *Let me be BLUNT: You're RUDE and IMPOLITE!* OK, not really—I'm sure you're a nice person. However, when you read that sentence, what thoughts came to your mind? In thinking about your response, refer to the study done by Bargh, Chen, and Burrows (1996) that's described on page 88.

Potential Sources of Error in Social Cognition: Why Total Rationality Is Rarer Than You Think

> ## Negativity Bias: The Tendency to Pay Extra Attention to Negative Information

1. *I'm sure you're doing well in school. Perhaps you're even on your school's honor roll? But I bet you're going to fail your social psychology course.* (OK, there I go again! I really don't have a sadistic streak, honest! And, of course, I'm sure you'll do just fine in your social psychology course.) But, think about it, what aspect of those three sentences in italics "stood out" for you? Even though there were two flattering statements made, I'm sure it was the last sentence. Explain how the nature of the negativity bias may might to shed some light on this matter. Also, summarize the evidence that suggests that the negativity bias has a biological component.

➢ The Optimistic Bias: Our Tendency to See the World through Rose-Colored Glasses

1. Do you remember that old song from the 1980s, *Don't Worry, Be Happy?* Discuss how the optimistic bias tends to make us to do just that—not to worry and to be happy.

2. When you're planning your work for an assignment, you may give an overly optimistic prediction as to how long it will take you to complete your work. Name the effect that is *most* closely associated with this behavior and briefly note why this effect occurs.

3. In your own words, what is the "bracing for loss" effect? Why does it occur?

➢ The Potential Costs of Thinking Too Much: Why, Sometimes, Our Tendency to Do as Little Cognitive Work as Possible May Be Justified

1. Given that you are in a college or university environment where you are encouraged to think carefully and thoroughly about ideas, it might seem odd—or even just "wrong"—to think that engaging in rational thought may backfire on us and cause problems. But, in fact, it really can backfire on us and cause problems. Explain why this is the case.

➤ Counterfactual Thinking: The Effects of Considering "What Might Have Been"

1. *Going up....going down.* Listed below are three different scenarios. For each scenario, note whether it illustrates an *upward* or *downward* counterfactual and whether its net effect on the individual will be positive or negative.

   a.) After dating Rachael for almost a year, Isaac told her that "he wasn't sure" if he loved her. Five years later, he still thinks about his statement.

   b.) Oliver, an ice skating Olympic athlete, has just won a silver medal after imagining winning a gold one.

   c.) Seth, an entrepreneur, was reflecting on his decision to not merge his business with another company a year ago.

2. What is "inaction inertia" and why does it occur?

➤ Magical Thinking: Would You Eat a Chocolate Shaped Like a Spider?

1. a.) Magical thinking involves assumptions that _____.

   b.) For each of the following examples, denote the principle of magical thinking that is being depicted:

   i. Ken is reluctant to rent an apartment where an AIDS patient formerly lived.

   ii. Professor Jones has brought a jello mold in the shape of a brain to class for her biology students to eat. She's surprised when very few students seem interested in having some.

   iii. Jon couldn't believe it when another terrorist attack occurred after he thought that another such attack was inevitable.

➢ **Thought Suppression: Why Efforts to Avoid Certain Thinking Certain Thoughts Sometimes Backfire**

1. *Think about your first romantic "crush." Now, try **not** thinking about your first romantic "crush" whatsoever.* Given the nature of thought suppression, why might such an exercise be extremely difficult to do?

2. Individuals who are _____ tend to be a particular risk for the negative effects associated with being unable to suppress one's thoughts.

➢ **Beyond The Headlines: As Social Psychologists See It...How The Criminal Justice System Could Be Improved—But Isn't: The Potential Role of Cognitive Biases**

1. State the three behaviors that lawyers and police officers incorrectly assume that most people are able to do well.

➤ Social Cognition: A Word of Optimism

1. Despite our tendency to make many errors in social thought, your text authors maintain that there is reason to believe that we can often successfully process information. Why do they believe this? Do you agree?

Affect and Cognition: How Feelings Shape Thought and Thought Shapes Feelings

➤ The Influence of Affect on Cognition

1. *I second that emotion!* Emotions and affect obviously can impact people in many ways. Three such ways involve mood-dependent memory, mood congruence effects, and mental contamination. For each of the scenarios below, denote which of these three processes is being illustrated:

    a.) Suzy is in a good mood and, as such, she vividly recalls a compliment that someone made to her.

    b.) Ed, a juror in a criminal case, realizes that he shouldn't allow a certain aspect of the defendant's testimony to influence his decision (as instructed by the judge), but he can't help but think about it.

    c.) Carl remembers learning some very favorable news on the day he learned about the Civil War in his American history class. On the day of his history exam, he finds himself in a good mood since his parents are taking him on a ski trip later that day; consequently, he gets all of the questions on his exam about the Civil War correct.

    d.) Barbara is in a foul mood since she had a big fight with her friend. When one of her co-workers mentioned that she looked "tired," she paid particular attention to this comment.

➢ **Social Psychology: Thirty Years of Progress...The Effects of Being in a Good Mood on Social Behavior and Social Cognition: From "The Warm Glow of Success" to the Effects of Mood on Heuristic Thinking**

1. Compare and contrast how social psychologists believed being in a good mood influenced social behavior and social cognition thirty years ago (Then) versus the more current views on this topic (Now).

        <u>Then</u>   <u>Now</u>

➢ **The Influence of Cognition on Affect**

1. Complete the sentences below in order to the make these true:

There are three ways by which cognition can influence affect. First, the _____-factor

theory of emotion suggests that we often don't know our own feelings or attitudes directly; because

these internal reactions tend to ambiguous, we infer their nature from _____.

Another way is through the activation of _____ containing a strong affective

component. A third way in which thoughts can influence feelings involves our efforts to

_____ our emotions.

Thinking about The Aftermath of the September 11, 2001 Attacks and Social Cognition

As you know, the World Trade Center was the target of a major terrorist attack in 1993. From that time on, many leading politicians and scholars warned that an even more serious and catastrophic terrorist attack in the United States was inevitable. Looking back on the events of September eleventh, do you feel that such warnings were self-fulfilling prophecies? Why?

After you read . . . Practice Tests

Practice Test 1

1. When we exceed our capacity to process new information, we enter a state of
   a. information overload.
   b. cognitive confusion.
   c. perseverance.
   d. mood congruence.

2. In making a judgment about a specific event, people often fail to take into account how likely the event occurs by ignoring
   a. suppressed thoughts.
   b. base-rates.
   c. priming effects.
   d. heuristics.

3. When my judgment of whether someone is aggressive is determined by how many relevant instances of aggressive behavior I can recall, I am using _____ to make my judgment.
    a. the representativeness heuristic
    b. a stereotype
    c. visual imagery
    d. the availability heuristic

4. When planting certain ideas in people's minds causes them to use these ideas to interpret subsequent events, this illustrates
    a. priming.
    b. the representativeness heuristic.
    c. the availability heuristic.
    d. an optimistic bias.

5. Suppose John received a B in his class—just barely missing an A; John's friend, Art, just barely received a B. As such, John will probably engage in _____ counterfactual thinking and be relatively _____.
    a. downward; satisfied
    b. upward; dissatisfied
    c. downward; dissatisfied
    d. upward; satisfied

6. A computer that Mary really wanted was on sale at 50% off, but she was too busy to get to the store. Now, it's on sale again at 25% off. Consistent with counterfactual thinking research, Mary will likely
    a. not buy it since it will remind her of when it was 50% off.
    b. buy it so she won't feel bad when it goes off sale again.
    c. question her judgment and, in doing so, will not show action inertia.
    d. wait to see whether any of her friends purchase the computer before she decides whether to purchase one.

7. Even though Joan loves chocolate, she refuses to eat a piece of chocolate shaped like a spider. This illustrates
    a. the representativeness heuristic.
    b. the negativity bias.
    c. counterfactual thinking.
    d. magical thinking.

8. A rebound effect typically occurs when we
    a. finish appraising our emotions.
    b. try to recover from a negative mood.
    c. have suppressed an intrusive thought.
    d. have been presented with information that contradicts our schema.

9. Unwanted intrusive thoughts occur most often for
    a. low reactance persons allowed to express their thoughts in writing.
    b. high reactance persons allowed to express their thoughts in writing.
    c. low reactance persons instructed to suppress intrusive thoughts.
    d. high reactance persons instructed to suppress intrusive thoughts.

10. Tim, a juror in a court case, will be highly impacted (in terms of his views of a defendant) when information is
    a. neutral and said to be admissible.
    b. neutral and was to be ignored.
    c. emotion-provoking and said to be admissible.
    d. emotion-provoking and to be ignored.

Practice Test 2

1. The term used by most social psychologists to describe our current feelings and mood is
    a. emotion.
    b. sentiment.
    c. effect.
    d. affect.

2. Information that we notice refers to
    a. attention.
    b. encoding.
    c. decoding.
    d. retrieval.

3. Mary feels very strongly that there is just one way to be a mother and she finds that she will not and cannot change her view even when presented with contradictory information. This illustrates the
    a. perseverance effect.
    b. availability heuristic.
    c. representativeness heuristic.
    d. self-fulfilling prophecy.

4. According to your text, an historical example of the negative effects of a self-fulfilling prophecy would relate to the events of the
    a. Holocaust.
    b. Great Depression.
    c. Watergate scandal.
    d. Vietnam War.

5. We often adopt and use heuristics due to the reality of
   a. the perseverance effect.
   b. cognitive laziness.
   c. information overload.
   d. schema-consistent information.

6. Suppose that on every September eleventh, you think about the September 11, 2001 terrorist attacks on America—in large part due to the high amount of media focus. The key reason for this intense recollection would be due to
   a. the availability heuristic.
   b. priming.
   c. automatic processing.
   d. the negativity effect.

7. We tend to have a greater sensitivity to information that is
   a. positive.
   b. negative.
   c. neutral.
   d. confusing.

8. Suppose a group of city developers in Chicago outline a very ambitious building plan and are stunned when, a year later, they only accomplished a quarter of what they had hoped to do up to this point. This illustrates the
   a. bracing for loss effect.
   b. optimistic bias.
   c. negativity bias.
   d. planning fallacy.

9. An important implication and application of the Wilson and Schooler (1991) study in which individuals were asked to rate the quality of certain jams is that
   a. thinking systematically and rationally is always critical.
   b. careful thought can be overdone.
   c. it is impossible to engage in "too much" careful thought when evaluating an issue.
   d. seemingly trivial issues should require more systematic thought than we might think is needed otherwise.

10. An example of a profession where it is *not* common for counterfactual thinking to regularly occur is with respect to
    a. entrepreneurship.
    b. the medical community.
    c. the legal community.
    d. teaching professionals.

Practice Test 3

1. Inaction inertia refers to
   a. the decision to not take an action and consequently, lose the opportunity for a positive outcome.
   b. the decision to not take an action and consequently, avoid the possibility of a negative outcome.
   c. a situation where the total number of upward counterfactuals equals the total number of downward counterfactuals.
   d. a situation where we refuse to take an action because we have taken many actions in the recent past.

2. Suppose Bob doesn't want to rent an apartment that previously housed an AIDS patient and Jill doesn't want to drink a liquid that looks like human blood (even though it's fruit punch). Which of the following statements *best* summarizes Bob and Jill's behaviors as these pertain to magical thinking?
   a. Bob and Jill are demonstrating the law of contagion.
   b. Bob and Jill are demonstrating the law of similarity.
   c. Bob is demonstrating the law of contagion and Jill is demonstrating the law of similarity.
   d. Jill is demonstrating the law of contagion and Bob is demonstrating the law of similarity.

3. The two components of thought suppression are
   a. repression and denial.
   b. effortful and systematic thinking.
   c. low and high reactance.
   d. a monitoring and an operating process.

4. The fact that the criminal justice system hasn't adopted changes in terms of how eyewitnesses examine a police lineup is consistent with the point that
   a. the criminal justice system has purposely chosen to reject social psychological research in this area.
   b. those in the criminal justice system are operating on various social cognitive biases of their own.
   c. those in the criminal justice system are incapable of changing the system—even if they wanted to.
   d. traditional police lineups typically yield extremely accurate identifications from eyewitnesses.

5. Which of the following statements regarding affect and cognition is *true*?
   a. Our feelings influence our cognitions only.
   b. Our cognitions influence our feelings only.
   c. Our cognitions and feelings influence one another.
   d. There is no relationship between our feelings and cognitions.

6. Consistent with ____, when we are in a bad mood, we tend to notice and remember ____ information.
   a. mood-dependent memory; positive
   b. mood-dependent memory; negative
   c. mood congruence effects; positive
   d. mood congruence effects; negative

7. Mental contamination is a type of mental processing that tends to be
   a. conscious and controllable.
   b. unconscious and controllable.
   c. conscious and uncontrollable.
   d. unconscious and uncontrollable.

8. Which of the following statements *best* summarizes the relationship between being in a good mood and helping behavior?
   a. Being in a good mood always increases helpfulness.
   b. Those in a good mood are no more likely to help others than those in a bad mood.
   c. Even though being in good mood makes one more likely to help others, this factor does not always increase helpfulness.
   d. There is a curvilinear relationship between mood and helping.

9. When we yield to temptation and engage in "forbidden pleasures," this is usually done
   a. in an unconscious matter.
   b. to stabilize negative feelings of distress.
   c. in a strategic fashion.
   d. because it does not involve high costs to our well-being.

10. Of the following, the study of _____ represents an issue of key concern in social cognition.
   a. helping behavior
   b. aggression
   c. attributions
   d. group behavior

Comprehensive Test
(NOTE: Items 1-15 are multiple-choice questions and items 16-23 are true-false questions.)

1. Cognition and our general cognitive capacities are
   a. rarely effortless and unlimited.
   b. rarely effortless and limited.
   c. often effortless and unlimited.
   d. often effortless and limited.

2. A "restaurant schema" would likely describe
   a. how one generally acts and is treated in a dining situation.
   b. how culture influences the eating habits of others.
   c. when it is appropriate to think about the rules of proper etiquette.
   d. why an individual decides to dine in a particular restaurant.

3. ____ refers to what information we notice.
   a. Retrieval
   b. Attention
   c. Encoding
   d. Decoding

4. Jamie tries to go on a diet but feels that is doomed to fail—and she does. This is consistent with a
   a. perseverance effect.
   b. negativity bias.
   c. self-fulfilling prophecy.
   d. controlled processing effect.

5. ____ helps to explain why many people fear flying, even though driving an automobile is statistically more dangerous.
   a. Automatic priming
   b. The representativeness heuristic
   c. The availability heuristic
   d. The planning fallacy

6. Automatic is to controlled as
   a. conscious is to effortful.
   b. nonconscious is to effortless.
   c. nonconscious is to effortful.
   d. conscious is to effortless.

7. We tend to pay particular attention to a facial expression depicting
   a. sadness.
   b. happiness.
   c. threatening anger.
   d. a neutral emotion.

8. The planning fallacy is an example of the
   a. optimistic bias.
   b. negativity bias.
   c. bracing for loss effect.
   d. mental contamination effect.

9. To think about "what might have been" is to engage in
   a. counterfactual thinking.
   b. magical thinking.
   c. thought suppression.
   d. automatic processing.

10. The act of suppressing one's thoughts
    a. is rarely successful.
    b. can be successful if information overload or fatigue is not present.
    c. can be successful if information overload or fatigue is present.
    d. appears to be unrelated to individual difference characteristics.

11. The authors of your text conclude that our ability to make sense of social information is
    a. hopelessly flawed.
    b. can be improved in such a way that we will not make too many errors.
    c. rarely subject to potential sources of bias.
    d. fairly impressive, despite errors.

12. Consistent with ____, those in a good mood tend to notice and remember ____ information.
    a. mood congruence effects; positive
    b. mood congruence effects; negative
    c. mood-dependent memory; positive
    d. mood-dependent memory; negative

13. A process where our judgments, emotions, or behaviors are influenced by unconscious, uncontrollable mental processing is called ____.
    a. automatic contamination
    b. mental contamination
    c. reactance processing
    d. emotional contamination

14. Polly is in a good mood, but her friend Anna is in a bad mood. As such, which of the following statements is *true*?
    a. Polly and Anna will show an increase in their likelihood of using mental shortcuts.
    b. Only Polly will show an increase in her likelihood of using mental shortcuts.
    c. Only Anna will show an increase her likelihood of using mental shortcuts.
    d. Polly and Anna will show a decrease in their likelihood of using mental shortcuts.

15. The ____-factor theory of emotion suggests that we don't know our feelings or attitudes directly.
    a. one
    b. two
    c. three
    d. four

16. Since information inconsistent with our schemas is readily noticed, it is guaranteed that this information will influence later social thought.

17. Most people incorrectly believe that words starting with the letter, "K," are more common than words in which "K" is the third letter.

18. Raters who carefully analyzed the reasons for their ratings of various strawberry jams more closely matched the ratings of experts than those who simply rated the jams.

19. Efforts to prevent certain thoughts from entering consciousness is referred to as thought repression.

20. To determine whether someone is a coach, I compare his traits to the "average" coach." In doing so, I am using the availability heuristic.

21. An AIDS patient's sweater will be rated less favorably even if it is kept in a sealed plastic bag and never touched by its owner.

22. The tendency to underestimate the time needed to complete a major project is known as the planning fallacy.

23. On the day that Darla learned certain facts about Abraham Lincoln in school, she had a headache. On the day of her school's quiz bowl, she also has a headache—but is surprised when she is able to correctly answer certain facts about Abraham Lincoln. This illustrates mood-dependent memory.

When You Have Finished . . .

TOP TEN REASONS WHY SOCIAL COGNITION HAS GREAT RELEVANCE FOR *YOUR* LIFE

1. By understanding our cognitions limitations and tendencies to make related errors, we may be in a better position to try and avoid such cognitive pitfalls.

2. We often try to *not* think about something when we don't want to deal with it. For instance, if you're on a diet, you may be trying very hard to avoid thinking about food. By understanding the limits of thought suppression, we may be better equipped to cope with unpleasant or unproductive thoughts.

3. Since we are prone to making the planning fallacy, we should try and reason our limitations in a realistic fashion so that we won't disappoint others—or ourselves.

4. By understanding how affect can influence memory and cognition, we are in a better position to maximize our memory skills and capabilities.

5. Given the prevalence of social cognition errors, we shouldn't be overly self-critical when and if we make such errors.

Consider the following exercise that relates to point #2: Pick a day where you have made a conscious decision to *not* think about a certain friend or acquaintance of yours. Then keep track of how many times during that day you actually think of that person. Contrast the number of thoughts you've had about this person with how often (on average) you thought about this person prior to conducting this exercise.

Short Answer/Essay Questions

1. **The Nature of Schemas**
   Briefly offer the most accurate understanding of whether we remember information consistent or inconsistent with our schemas.

2. **Heuristics**
   Contrast how the representativeness heuristic differs from the availability heuristic.

3. **Biases in Cognition**
   Suppose you are candidate for a job where four individuals are conducting an individual. You notice that each of these individuals shows a distinct facial expression: one is smiling, one appears to be sad, another appears to have a threatening expression, and the fourth person doesn't appear to be showing any emotional expression. For which of these expressions will you be *most* apt to quickly recognize the emotion in question? Why?

4. **Magical Thinking**
   Provide a brief overview of the three principles of magical thinking.

5. **Affect and Cognition**
   Detail at least three ways that affect can influence cognition by explaining how these processes operate.

4 ATTITUDES:
EVALUATING THE SOCIAL WORLD

Before you read . . .

This chapter discusses an issue in which you have had much exposure even before taking your social psychology course—the study of attitudes, or evaluations of various aspects of the social world. We'll begin our consideration of this topic with a discussion of how attitudes develop and the general purposes that these often serve. You will also read about when and how attitudes can influence behavior. Afterward, you will find out about ways to persuade others and why, under certain conditions, such attempts may fail. You'll also be introduced to the study of cognitive dissonance or what happens when we show inconsistent attitudes or a gap between our attitudes and behavior. As part of this discussion, you'll consider why cognitive dissonance often produces attitude change and how it can actually be used to produce benefits for individuals.

Chapter Objectives

After reading this chapter, you should be able to:

- Describe what attitudes are and why these are of interest to social psychologists.

- Outline the ways in which we may acquire attitudes through learning.

- Identify the role that genetics plays in attitude acquisition.

- Discuss the basic functions that attitudes may serve.

- Outline when and how attitudes may affect behavior from a historical and contemporary social psychological perspective.

- Describe the aspects of attitudes and how these may influence behavior.

- Summarize how the theories of reasoned action and planned behavior and the attitude-to-behavior process model try to understand the attitude-behavior link.

- State the key factors that social psychologists have historically believed lead to successful persuasion.

- Contrast systematic and heuristic processing in terms of how these relate to persuasion.

- Describe why and how we may resist persuasion by discussing reactance, forewarning, selective avoidance, biased assimilation, and attitude polarization.

- Consider when we experience cognitive dissonance, how we can reduce it, and whether it is unpleasant for most individuals.

- Understand the less-leads-to-more effect by paying particular attention to the famous Festinger and Carlsmith (1959) study.

- Explain how hypocrisy can be used in a manner that produces beneficial effects for an individual.

As you read . . .

> Remember this! Below are a list of some of the key terms and concepts from this chapter. Make flashcards in order to enhance your recall ability of these terms. Refer to the definitions that are either in boldface or in the margins of this chapter for help. Be advised that you may also want to include additional terms from this chapter as you deem necessary.

Attitudes	Attitude ambivalence	Social learning
Classical conditioning	Subliminal conditioning	Instrumental conditioning
Observational learning	Social comparison	The functions of attitudes
Attitude origins	Attitude strength and its components	Attitude specificity
Theory of reasoned action	Theory of planned behavior	Behavioral intentions
Subjective norms	Perceived behavioral control	Attitude-to-behavior process model
Persuasion	One- vs. two-sided approach	Systematic vs. heuristic processing
Central vs. peripheral route	Elaboration likelihood model	Reactance
Forewarning	Selective avoidance	Biased assimilation
Attitude polarization	Hostile media bias	Cognitive dissonance
Trivialization	Spreading of alternatives effect	Less-leads-to-more effect
Hypocrisy		

Attitude Formation: How—and Why—Attitudes Develop

➤ Social Learning: Acquiring Attitudes from Others

1. In your own words, what is an "attitude?" Also, what does it mean when we show "attitude ambivalence?"

2. Match it! Match each phrase, word, or sentence on the left side of the page with an identifying concept on the right side of the page. Note that each item on the right should be used ONLY ONCE.

_____1. Strengthening outcomes with rewards   A. social learning

_____2. Learning by viewing others' actions   B. classical conditioning

_____3. Carried out in order to determine the correctness of our   C. subliminal conditioning
   views of social reality.

_____4. Involves exposure to a stimulus below a person's threshold   D. instrumental conditioning
   of conscious awareness.

_____5. The process through which we acquire new information   E. observational learning
   from others.

_____6. Conscious learning in which a neutral stimulus becomes a   F. social comparison
   signal for the presentation of another stimulus.

➤ Genetic Factors: Some Surprising Findings

1. *What's wrong here?* Each of the following statements is *false*. Modify some aspect of the statement in order to make it *true*.

   a. Genetic factors are the most significant factor in the development of attitudes.

   b. The attitudes of identical twins correlate more highly than those of nonidentical twins, only if they were raised together.

   c. Attitudes that are more cognitive in nature appear to be particularly heritable.

➢ Attitude Functions: Why We Form Attitudes in the First Place

1. *Guess who's coming to dinner?* Imagine that you're at a dinner party and you overhear the statements below from different people. Identify the apparent function of each of these attitudes and explain your reasoning.

He told you I was racist! Oh no, I've never even thought a single racial slur in my life!

_____

_____

_____

Oh, so you say that you work for a law firm—I think lawyers do an incredible service to society!

I am proud to call myself a liberal!

_____   _____

_____   _____

_____   _____

➢ The Attitude-Behavior Link: When—and How—Attitudes Influence Behavior

1. In considering the attitude-behavior link, social psychologists now focus on the question, _____

_____, and no longer the question,

_____.

ATTITUDES

> ## Social Psychology: Thirty Years of Progress…Studying the Attitude-Behavior Link

1. Compare and contrast how social psychologists conceptualized the attitude-behavior link (in this case rather than thirty years ago) in the 1930s (Then) versus the more current views on this topic (Now).

         Then   Now

> ## When Do Attitudes Influence Behavior? Specificity, Strength, Accessibility, and Other

1. Word scramble! Who said studying can't be fun? Unscramble the following six words below. Use the hints if you're having trouble unscrambling the words. When you unscramble the six words, unscramble the letters contained in the brackets to reveal the "bonus" word. Have fun!

a. RMNETCAIO   ___ ___ ___ [___] ___ ___ ___ ___ ___ ___

b. TENTSHRG   ___ ___ [___] ___ ___ ___ ___ ___

c. CITYCIEFPS   ___ ___ ___ ___ [___] ___ ___ ___ ___ ___

d. WODEKENG   ___ ___ ___ ___ ___ ___ ___ [___] ___

e. SEYNITTIN   [___] ___ ___ ___ ___ ___ ___ ___ ___

f. TONCTRSINA   ___ ___ [___] ___ ___ ___ ___ ___ ___ ___

*BONUS WORD: _____

Hints:
a. How much a person cares about an issue.
b. This term incorporates many factors.
c. An attitude that's isn't too general, yet it greatly predicts behavior.
d. One's awareness of the attitude object.
e. The level of emotional reaction caused by the attitude object.
f. A situational _____ can moderate the relationship between attitudes and behavior.
BONUS: Pertains to how attitudes are formed.

➤ How Do Attitudes Influence Behavior? Intentions, Willingness, and Action

1. Identify the components of the theories of reasoned action and planned behavior. Which components are unique to each theory?

2. State below the factors that predict the intention to use versus the actual use of the drug ecstasy.

<u>Intention to use</u>   <u>Actual Use</u>

3. In the attitude-to-behavior process model, some event activates an attitude that, in turn, influences

_____. At the same time, _____

_____ is also activated. Together, _____

_____ shape our definitions of the

event. Ultimately, this perception influences our _____.

➤ **Biased Assimilation and Attitude Polarization: "If It's Contrary to What I Believe, Then It Must Be Unreliable or Worse!"**

1. Pin the tail on the process! For each of the following statements provided by a hypothetical person below, denote whether it illustrates biased assimilation, attitude polarization, or the hostile media bias.

   a.) "I don't like Channel 404's news because it's too conservative—so, therefore, it must be biased!"

   b.) "Even though Joe said that stock in that company is worthless, I think he's unreliable."

   c.) "I didn't like Bernadette before, but after hearing the latest rumors about her, I hate her!"

Cognitive Dissonance: Why Our Behavior Can Sometimes Influence Our Attitudes

---

➤ **Cognitive Dissonance: What It Is and Various Ways (Direct and Indirect) to Reduce It**

1. In your own words, describe what is meant by "cognitive dissonance."

2. Complete the chart below by listing the various direct and indirect approaches to dissonance reduction.

Direct Approaches	Indirect Approaches

3. Describe the evidence that suggests that dissonance really is, in fact, an unpleasant state.

4. Summarize the evidence that considers whether dissonance is a universal human experience.

> ## Beyond The Headlines: As Social Psychologists See It…When a Physical Addiction and Dissonance Collide, Guess Which Wins?

1. Identify some of the ways smokers reduce their dissonance regarding their unhealthy habit. Also, what's the *best* technique for reducing this dissonance?

> ## **Dissonance and Attitude Change: The Effects of Induced Compliance**

1. Suppose an American is kidnapped by a group of terrorists and subsequently releases a statement whereby he denounces America. Why should we *not* really believe that the hostage holds these views?

2. Describe the dynamics of the famous Festinger and Carlsmith (1959) study and, in doing so, discuss the relevance of the less-leads-to-more effect.

> ## **Dissonance as a Tool for Beneficial Changes in Behavior: When Hypocrisy Can Be a Force for Good**

1. Outline the three elements that need to be in place if one is to successfully use dissonance in order to generate hypocrisy to bring about positive changes.

Thinking about The Aftermath of the September 11, 2001 Attacks and Attitudes

In the immediate aftermath of the attacks, there were many reports suggesting that Americans were more readily engaging in positive behaviors that they may have been neglecting in their lives, such as reconsidering what is important in life, reconnecting with close others, and increased patriotism. Think of someone whom you know (perhaps even yourself) who showed such positive changes in the wake of the disaster—but has now reverted back to his or her old ways. How might you use hypocrisy in a manner that produces beneficial effects for this person?

After you read . . . Practice Tests

Practice Test 1

1. Compared to attitudes acquired through indirect experience, attitudes acquired through direct experience
   a. are the basis for slower, more deliberate responses.
   b. exert stronger effects on behavior.
   c. are held with less confidence.
   d. are weaker.

2. When LaPiere examined questionnaire responses and behavioral reports from a touring Chinese couple in the 1930s, he found that most restaurants indicated that they
   a. would serve a Chinese couple and actually served them.
   b. would not serve a Chinese couple and actually did not serve them.
   c. would serve a Chinese couple but refused service.
   d. would not serve a Chinese couple but actually served them.

3. Which of the following statements about the relationship between attitudes and behaviors is *true*?
   a. Accurate predictions of overt behavior can often be derived from people's specific attitudes.
   b. Attitudes formed as a result of direct experience with the attitude object are poor predictors of behavior.
   c. The more general one's attitudes, the greater the accuracy in predicting specific behaviors.
   d. Attitudes do not predict behavior.

4. Whether a student will actually undergo body piercing to wear a nose ring is best predicted by the ____ and how one reacts to a panhandler who approached them on the street is best predicted by the ____.
   a. theory of planned behavior; attitude-to-behavior process model
   b. attitude-to-behavior process model; theory of planned behavior
   c. theory of planned behavior; theory of planned behavior also
   d. attitude-to-behavior process model; attitude-to-behavior process model also

5. Which of the following statements about persuasion is *false*?
   a. Experts are more persuasive than non-experts.
   b. People who speak slowly are more persuasive than those who speak rapidly.
   c. Persuasion can be enhanced by fear-arousing messages.
   d. It is sometimes easier to persuade a person who's distracted from a message than one paying full attention.

6. The ____ route is used when attitudes are changed without careful thought about the issue or arguments being used.
   a. peripheral
   b. central
   c. elaborative
   d. heuristic

7. According to the elaboration likelihood model, a persuader with strong, convincing arguments should use the ____ route.
   a. peripheral
   b. central
   c. elaborative
   d. heuristic

8. An attitude serves a ____ function when it helps a person to organize and interpret diverse information.
   a. self-identity
   b. self-esteem
   c. knowledge
   d. self-expression

9. Due to ____, a person may resist persuasion attempts since it directs their attention away from information that challenges their existing attitudes.
    a. reactance
    b. forewarning
    c. biased assimilation
    d. selective avoidance

10. An example of how to use hypocrisy to modify one's attitudes would be to
    a. get people to say something they don't believe.
    b. get people to encourage others to do some beneficial action and then remind them that they don't always perform that behavior themselves.
    c. simply get people to encourage others to do some beneficial action.
    d. simply remind people that they don't always perform beneficial actions.

Practice Test 2

1. We tend to experience attitude ambivalence when we
    a. don't feel passionate about an issue.
    b. hold positive and negative evaluations of the same attitude object.
    c. are in disagreement with a close other over some issue.
    d. don't feel fully informed about an attitude object.

2. Mary asks her friend about her views on the crisis in the Middle East in order to evaluate her own feelings on the matter. This example illustrates ____.
    a. observational learning
    b. social comparison
    c. instrumental conditioning
    d. classical conditioning

3. Some preliminary research suggests that attitudes involving gut-level preferences are
    a. unrelated to genetic factors.
    b. more strongly influenced by genetic factors than attitudes about complex issues.
    c. less strongly influenced by genetic factors than attitudes about complex issues.
    d. just as likely to be influenced by genetic factors than attitudes about complex issues.

4. Attitudes are usually conceptualized as serving all of the following functions, *except*
    a. impression motivation.
    b. depression barrier.
    c. self-identity.
    d. ego-defensive.

5. Even though Bob isn't pleased with the quality of his hamburger, he decides to not complain about it to his waitress for fear of spoiling the festive time he is having with his friends. This example illustrates that _____ often moderate the relationship between attitudes and behavior.
   a. complex genetic factors
   b. attitude origins
   c. individual differences
   d. situational constraints

6. Attitude strength incorporates all of the following elements, *except*
   a. reliability.
   b. accessibility.
   c. intensity.
   d. knowledge.

7. The extent to which attitudes are focused on particular objects or situations is known as
   a. attitude strength.
   b. attitude origin.
   c. attitude specificity.
   d. attitude reasonability.

8. The component(s) that comprise the theories of reasoned action and planned behavior is (are)
   a. attitudes toward a given behavior and subjective norms about it.
   b. subjective norms about a given behavior and perceived behavioral control.
   c. attitudes toward a given behavior and perceived behavioral control.
   d. attitudes toward a given behavior.

9. The importance of social norms tends to be particularly emphasized in the
   a. theory of planned behavior.
   b. theory of reasoned action.
   c. attitude-to-behavior process model.
   d. central route to persuasion.

10. Suppose Josh is about to give a speech to an audience whose views are fairly contrary to his own. In order to be *most* persuasive, he should adopt a _____ approach.
    a. one-sided
    b. two-sided
    c. muddled
    d. non-emotional

Practice Test 3

1. Systematic processing is to heuristic processing as
   a. careful is to simple.
   b. careless is to careful.
   c. complete is to accurate.
   d. incomplete is to complete.

2. Of the following professions, the one that is *most* associated with the use of heuristic processing is a
   a. doctor.
   b. salesperson.
   c. professor.
   d. newspaper reporter.

3. _____ is defined as a negative reaction to threats to one's personal freedom.
   a. Forewarning
   b. Selective avoidance
   c. Reactance
   d. Biased assimilation

4. Paul is attending a town meeting. When he hears a speaker with whom he disagrees, he decided to leave the room. This example illustrates
   a. forewarning.
   b. selective avoidance.
   c. reactance.
   d. biased assimilation.

5. Which of the following cognitions by a television news viewer *best* illustrates the hostile media bias?
   a. "TV news today just can't get the story right!"
   b. "You can't believe anything that's said on television—that's why I read the newspaper."
   c. "I sure love how those TV news hosts duke it out when debating issues!"
   d. "Since that channel is so out of line with my views, it must be biased!"

6. Cognitive dissonance typically occurs when
   a. we have inconsistent attitudes.
   b. there is a discrepancy between our attitudes and behaviors.
   c. either we have inconsistent attitudes or there is a discrepancy between our attitudes and behaviors.
   d. we are unsure of how we think about some issue.

7. The process of trivialization is a(n) _____ approach that tends to _____ dissonance.
   a. direct; reduce
   b. direct; increase
   c. indirect; reduce
   d. indirect; increase

8. Induced compliance tends to
   a. create a feeling of dissonance.
   b. not cause dissonance since such statements were made under duress.
   c. cause a person to solidify their own beliefs.
   d. reduce any previous feelings of dissonance.

9. The famous Festinger and Carlsmith (1959) study found that college students reported that they enjoyed a boring task
   a. regardless of how much they were paid.
   b. regardless of whether they were paid.
   c. when they were paid a large amount of money.
   d. when they were paid a small amount of money.

10. Which of the following statements about hypocrisy is *false*?
   a. It can be used a tool to change other's behaviors in desirable ways.
   b. It involves publicly advocating some attitude or behavior that's inconsistent with one's own attitudes or behaviors.
   c. If hypocrisy is used to try to change others' behaviors, then the individual in question must be made to feel an overwhelming sense of shame.
   d. People often show an great gap between their health-related attitudes and behaviors.

Comprehensive Test
(NOTE: Items 1-15 are multiple-choice questions and items 16-23 are true-false questions.)

1. Suppose Thomas, a seven year old, lives in Philadelphia. Whenever his parents see a panhandler, they frown in disgust. Consequently, Thomas develops very negative views of panhandlers. This example best illustrates
   a. classical conditioning.
   b. subliminal conditioning.
   c. instrumental conditioning.
   d. social learning.

2. Since most people feel better after they take an aspirin for a headache, this increases the likelihood that they will take aspirins again for future headaches. Thus, consistent with ____ conditioning, aspirin functions as a ____.
   a. classical; reward
   b. instrumental; reward
   c. classical; punishment
   d. instrumental; punishment

3. The attitudes of identical twins ____ correlate more highly than those of nonidentical twins ____ the identical twins where separated at birth.
   a. do; even if
   b. do; only if
   c. do; unless
   d. do not; regardless

4. Murray doesn't want to confront the fact that he's been cheating on his wife, so he develops a strong belief that adultery is "sinful." This example shows how attitudes often have a(n) ____ function.
   a. delusional
   b. self-esteem
   c. impression motivation
   d. ego-defensive

5. The key question that social psychologists currently try to focus on with respect to the attitude-behavior link is:
   a. "Are attitudes relevant to study?"
   b. "Do attitudes really exert any effects on behavior?"
   c. "When and how do attitudes influence behavior?"
   d. "Why don't attitudes inherently predict behavior?"

6. A very significant determinant of attitude importance is one's
   a. attitude ambivalence.
   b. parental influence.
   c. general interest.
   d. vested interest.

7. The importance of subjective norms is highlighted in the
   a. theory of planned behavior only.
   b. theory of reasoned action only.
   c. theories of planned behavior and reasoned action.
   d. theory of attitude-behavior reasons only.

8. In order to increase the likelihood that one will be successful at his or her attempts at persuasion, an individual should
   a. not present a message that makes it clear that one is trying to change others' attitudes.
   b. ensure that the audience will not be distracted by an extraneous event.
   c. speak as slowly as possible.
   d. avoid arousing strong emotions.

9. When we believe a message is important, it is quite likely that we'll engage in ____ processing via the ____ route.
   a. systematic; central
   b. systematic; peripheral
   c. heuristic; central
   d. heuristic; peripheral

10. ____, which tends to ____ resistance to persuasion, is defined as advance knowledge that one is about to become the target of an attempt at persuasion.
    a. Reactance; decrease
    b. Reactance; increase
    c. Forewarning; decrease
    d. Forewarning; increase

11. Upon learning of some news that was contrary to her opinions, Shelley viewed this information as unreliable and unconvincing. This example best depicts
    a. biased assimilation.
    b. attitude polarization.
    c. selective avoidance.
    d. cognitive dissonance.

12. Self-affirmation is to trivialization as
    a. indirect is to direct.
    b. direct is to indirect.
    c. helpful is to harmful.
    d. cognitive dissonance is to less-leads-to-more effect.

13. In terms of its impact on the operation of dissonance, cultural factors appear to be
    a. not terribly important.
    b. instrumental in determining whether someone feels uneasy about inconsistent thoughts.
    c. important in ascertaining the precise conditions under which these occur.
    d. irrelevant.

14. The term used to describe the fact that fewer reasons or rewards lead to more attitude change is called the
    a. more-leads-to-less-effect
    b. less-leads-to-more-effect.
    c. fewer-leads-to-greater-effect.
    d. greater-leads-to-fewer effect.

15. In order to use hypocrisy in an effective way that promotes beneficial changes, all of the following elements must be present, *except*
    a. the person in question must publicly advocate the desired behavior.
    b. the person in question must be given access to direct means for reducing his or her dissonance.
    c. the person in question needs to acknowledge his or her shortcomings as a person.
    d. the person in question must think about his or her own failures to show the beneficial behaviors in the past.

16. Genetic factors play just as much of a role in shaping "gut-level" preferences as in shaping other attitudes.

17. Consistent with the openly-expressed prejudice of the 1930s, a study conducted during this time period showed that most U.S. restaurants and hotels refused service to a young Chinese couple.

18. Attitudes tend to predict behavior when these are specific, rather than general.

19. A speaker who is trying to persuade someone should present both sides of the issue if the target is already in agreement with the message.

20. People who speak slowly tend to be more persuasive than those who speak rapidly.

21. Heuristic cues tend to be associated with the peripheral, rather than the central, route.

22. Selective exposure occurs when a person has advance knowledge that he or she is the target of a persuasion attempt.

23. In the famous Festinger and Carlsmith (1959) experiment, the more money subjects were paid to tell another person how interesting a boring experiment was, the more the subjects believed what they had said.

When You Have Finished . . .

TOP TEN REASONS WHY THE STUDY OF ATTITUDES HAS GREAT RELEVANCE FOR *YOUR* LIFE

1. We form attitudes about virtually every possible topic that has some degree of relevance to our lives. As such, we should be interested in how attitudes develop and influence behavior.

2. Since we often try to persuade others and vice-versa, an understanding of how persuasion works may make our efforts more viable while helping us to realize when others are trying to cause us to change our attitudes.

3. We can use dissonance in such a way to help promote healthy behaviors and lifestyles when it is related to a person's hypocrisy.

4. We often wonder whether a person's attitude will influence and predict their behaviors. By understanding the attitude-behavior link, we are more apt to make accurate predictions.

5. If you've ever wondered from where your own attitudes have originated, then consider looking at the attitudes of parents and other relatives, given the importance of social learning and genetics.

Let's revisit point #2. Watch an hour or two of prime time television (e.g., between 8-10 p.m.) and pay particular attention to the *television commercials*. For each commercial you see, decide the method of persuasion that's being used and rate this method on a 1 to 5 scale (where "5" is the *most* persuasive) consider how persuasive the commercial is to you.

Short Answer/Essay Questions

1. **Attitude Formation**
    What is the key difference between classical and subliminal conditioning?

2. **Attitude Functions**
   List and briefly discuss the main functions that attitudes serve.

3. **How Attitudes Influence Behavior**
   Discuss how Fazio's attitude-to-behavior model operates.

4. **Persuasion**
   Suppose you are giving a talk to a group of individuals who may hold views different than your own. What is an effective way to make your talk?

5. **Cognitive Dissonance and Hypocrisy**
   Suppose one of your friends usually doesn't wear his seat belt and you want to encourage him to do so. Briefly explain how you can use dissonance to help him change his behavior.

5

ASPECTS OF SOCIAL IDENTITY: SELF AND GENDER

Before you read . . .

This chapter considers two very important aspects of social identity—the self and gender. With respect to the study of the self, you'll consider the many unique components of your own identity by reviewing what is known as your self-concept. The general attitudes that you have about yourself in terms of your own worth or self-esteem will also be explored. You'll also be presented with an overview of other key dimensions of self-functioning, such as self-focusing, self-monitoring, and self-efficacy. The second part of this chapter considers the topic of gender. First of all, did you know that the terms, "sex" and "gender," do *not* have the same meaning? In this chapter, you'll find out why this is the case. You'll also have a good understanding of how we develop our gender identity and stereotypes and what the implications of these behaviors are for our lives. The chapter concludes with a consideration of why men and women sometimes do seem, at times, to come from different worlds: Is it due to biology, environmental factors, or both?

Chapter Objectives

After reading this chapter, you should be able to:

- Understand the components and dimensions of a person's social identity.

- State and define the three types of self-awareness.

- Consider how the self-concept functions and provide at least two examples of a specific type of self-concept.

- Describe how external factors can shape one's self-concept.

- Explain how we evaluate our self-esteem and how social comparison processes function in this respect.

- Contrast the consequences of low versus high self-esteem.

- Offer a definition of self-focusing and why this is important in our lives.

85

- Contrast the differences between low and high self-monitors.

- Discuss how self-efficacy affects our lives and offer some examples of specific types of self-efficacy.

- Explain the difference between the terms, "sex" and "gender."

- Outline the developmental aspects of gender identity.

- Understand the rationale behind the Bem Sex-Role Inventory and list the classifications that a person may have after completing this measure.

- Describe the consequences and reactions to gender-role behavior, including the benefits and disadvantages of these various gender-roles.

- Consider how gender roles at home and work may have varied or stayed constant over the past several decades.

- Contrast biological/evolutionary versus societal/environment perspectives as to why men and women often exhibit different behaviors.

As you read . . .

Remember this! Below are a list of some of the key terms and concepts from this chapter. Make flashcards in order to enhance your recall ability of these terms. Refer to the definitions that are either in boldface or in the margins of this chapter for help. Be advised that you may also want to include additional terms from this chapter as you deem necessary.

Social identity	Self-concept	Subjective, objective, and symbolic self-awareness
Self-reference effect	Sexual self-schema	Social self
Possible selves	Working self-concept	The Michelangelo phenomenon
Self-esteem	Self-assessment	Self-verification
Downward vs. upward social comparison	Paradoxical vs. variable self-esteem	Self-focusing
Compartmentalized self-organization	Self-monitoring	Self-efficacy
Sex vs. gender	Gender identity	Sex typing
Bem Sex-Role Inventory	Gender-role identification	Androgynous
Undifferentiated	Hypermasculinity	Hyperfemininity
Testosterone	Estrogen	

Social Identity: An Overview

1. State the components of our social identity.

The Self: Components of One's Unique Identity

➢ Self-Concept: The Basic Schema

1. OK, maybe it's not quite yet ready for the *New York Times* style crossword section, but it's a crossword puzzle nonetheless. Your clues are below—get to it!

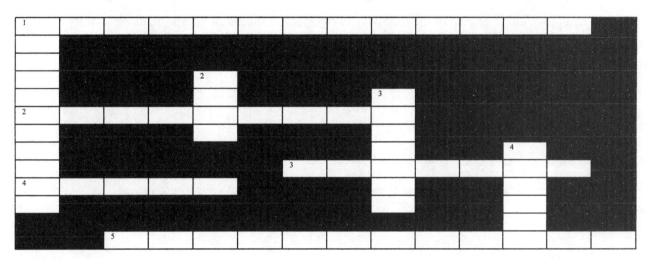

Across
1. Information about the self is processed more efficiently.
2. A form of self-awareness in which an organism is the object of its own attention.
3. At any given time we have a ___ self-concept.
4. Only men appear to have a sexual self-schema associated with aggression and ___.
5. One's partner as sculptor involves the ___ phenomenon.

Down
1. Organized collection of beliefs about the self.
2. An example of one of the components of the social self.
3. An extreme self-conception.
4. Individualistic cultures emphasize ___ aspects of the self.

> ## Self-Esteem: Attitudes about Oneself

1. In your own words, define "self-esteem."

2. State and describe the three possible motives for self-evaluation.

3. What's going on? For each of the following two scenarios, discuss what you're doing exactly, the impact of what you're doing is for your self-esteem, and why is this impact happening.

   a.) You're making a downward social comparison with a stranger....

   b.) You're making an upward social comparison with a member of your in-group...

5. Name that self-esteem! Complete the following chart by noting the key characteristics or effects associated with the particular type of self-esteem.

Self-Esteem	Key Characteristics/Effects
Low self-esteem	
High self-esteem	
Paradoxical self-esteem	
Variable self-esteem	

➤ Other Aspects of Self-Functioning: Focusing, Monitoring, and Efficacy

1. *Encore! Encore!* OK, so, you liked the last exercise, eh? Let's do a modified repeat of that exercise: Name that aspect of self-functioning! But to spice things up, this time I'll provide the key characteristics/effects and *you* name the aspect of self-functioning that's being described.

Aspect of Self-Functioning	Key Characteristics/Effects
	Engage in role playing in order to obtain positive evaluations from others
	Replaying the same thoughts over and over rather, than working on solutions
	The shared belief by a group that together they will produce a desired effect
	The ability to resist peer pressure and avoid high-risk activities

Gender: Being a Male or Female as a Crucial Aspect of Identity

➤ Sex and Gender

1. Why shouldn't we use the terms, "sex" and "gender," interchangeably?

➤ Gender Identity and Gender Stereotypes

1. Match it! Match each phrase, word, or sentence on the left side of the page with an identifying concept on the right side of the page. Note that each item on the right should be used *only once*.

____1. Understanding the stereotypes of being male and female in one's culture   A. gender identity

____2. Conscious awareness of this develops around age two   B. gender consistency

____3. An understanding of gender as a basic, enduring attribute   C. sex typing

➤ **Gender-Role Behavior and Reactions to Gender-Role Behavior**

1. Denote whether each of the following characteristics typically describes the typical male or female role, androgyny, hypermasculinity, or hyperfemininity.

   a. Acting in a dominant way: _____

   b. Sitting with one's upper legs against each other: _____

   c. Callous sexual attitudes: _____

   d. Sometimes saying "no" but meaning "yes": _____

   e. Being flexibility in coping with stress: _____

2. Complete the chart below by denoting gender role behavior in the past versus now. Highlight those areas, in particular, where there have been considerable changes.

Gender Roles Then	Gender Roles Now

> ## Social Psychology: Thirty Years of Progress...Sex, The Gender Revolution, and Related Issues

1. Compare and contrast how social psychologists have conceptualized issues pertaining to sex and gender thirty years ago (Then) versus the more current views on this topic (Now).

    Then   Now

2. State all of the possible gender-role identifications that a person could have after completing the Bem Sex-Role Inventory (BSRI).

> ## When Men and Women Differ: Biology, Acquired Gender Roles, or Both?

1. Summarize the key sex differences for men and women as a function of biology or evolution.

Men	Women

2. Girls tend to show more _____ than boys; a key reason for this is due to girls'

   and women's greater concern for _____.

➤ Beyond The Headlines: As Social Psychologists See It…Little Girls Beset by Bigger Worries

1. Why is appearance a major issue for women?

2. Consider whether there are cultural differences in terms of how women view their appearance.

Thinking about The Aftermath of the September 11, 2001 Attacks and Social Identity

All of us have been greatly affected by the September eleventh tragedy and the ongoing war on terrorism. Unless you were personally affected by these events (e.g., you lost a loved one in the attacks), you probably have been able to adjust fairly well in a post-September eleventh world. However, in the immediate aftermath of the attacks, many people were attempting to adjust to the reality of these events. In doing so, did you find yourself making upward or downward social comparisons? Looking back, did the way in which you coped with these events differ from how you usually cope with stressful events?

After you read . . . Practice Tests

Practice Test 1

1. One's definition of who he or she is including personal attributes is called
   a. personal identity.
   b. self identity.
   c. group identity.
   d. social identity.

2. With respect to our self-concept, we tend to do all of the following, *except*
   a. find excuses for any inconsistencies.
   b. maintain a level of self-consistency.
   c. question the efficacy of our motives.
   d. protect our self-image from threatening information.

3. Only humans appear to have _____ self-awareness.
   a. accurate
   b. symbolic
   c. subjective
   d. objective

4. The basic reason for the self-reference effect is that
   a. humans tend to be overly self-focused.
   b. self-relevant material is processed more efficiently.
   c. we typically are not able to process information that is irrelevant to the self.
   d. humans don't care about social information unless it directly pertains to them.

5. A major source of conflict in female sexuality tends to focus on
   a. being passionate/loving versus aggressive/domineering.
   b. positive and negative reactions to sexuality.
   c. the importance of being open and direct.
   d. whether it is important to have a sexual self-schema.

6. The social self consists of _____ key components.
   a. two
   b. three
   c. four
   d. five

7. Culture influences social self-concepts
   a. in very rare instances.
   b. such that the welfare of the group, rather than the individual, is emphasized in Western cultures.
   c. such that the welfare of the group, rather than the individual, is emphasized in Eastern cultures.
   d. only if an individual is living in a harsh environment of some sort.

8. _____ are mental representations of what we might become.
   a. Working self-concepts
   b. Unrealized selves
   c. Potential selves
   d. Possible selves

9. Suppose Peter, who just completed his Ph.D. in psychology, is now a professor. As such, he'll probably experience
   a. a change in one's self-concept.
   b. decreased self-esteem.
   c. the lack of a need for other possible selves.
   d. a stable self-image.

10. All of the following are motives for self-evaluation, *except*
   a. self-assessment.
   b. self-criticism.
   c. self-enhancement.
   d. self-verification.

Practice Test 2

1. Downward social comparisons tend to have _____ effect(s) on self-esteem and upward social comparisons tend to have _____ effect(s) on self-esteem when made with a stranger.
   a. positive; negative
   b. no; positive
   c. negative; no
   d. positive; no

2. Which of the following statements about self-esteem is *true*?
   a. Paradoxical self-esteem only refers to unrealistically high self-esteem.
   b. Low self-esteem has more negative consequences than variable self-esteem.
   c. Aggressive people typically have high self-esteem.
   d. Low self-esteem does not affect the body's immune system.

3. Rogers (1951) developed a therapeutic technique called _____ that is designed to boost one's self-esteem.
   a. conditional positive regard
   b. unconditional positive regard
   c. ideal-self imagery
   d. inherent self-regard

4. ____ is the act of directing attention toward oneself.
   a. Self-focusing
   b. Self-esteem
   c. Self-monitoring
   d. Self-efficacy

5. When Joan failed her art quiz, she continuously replayed the same thoughts over and over again as to why she failed. This is consistent with a(n) ____ orientation.
   a. reflective
   b. ruminative
   c. social
   d. inquisitive

6. Betty has a tendency to file positive and negative aspects of her experiences separately in memory. Her behavior illustrates ____.
   a. mood congruence effects
   b. mood-memory consistency effects
   c. compartmentalized self-organization
   d. self-focused affect orientation dimensions

7. High self-monitors tend to possess all of the following characteristics, *except*
   a. fewer and longer lasting romantic relationships.
   b. engaging in role playing in order to obtain positive evaluations from others.
   c. the use of third person when talking about themselves.
   d. more positive self-esteem.

8. A shared belief by members of a group that together they can produce desired effects is known as ____ self-efficacy.
   a. social
   b. collective
   c. general
   d. self-regulatory

9. The attributes and expectancies associated with whether one is male or female is referred to as
   a. sex.
   b. gender.
   c. sex or gender.
   d. neither sex nor gender.

10. Even if they aren't entirely sure what the words "girl" and "boy" mean, children typically begin to use one of those words to describes themselves at around ____ of age.
    a. eighteen months
    b. two years
    c. three years
    d. four years

Practice Test 3

1. Jason, a five-year-old, now understands that gender is a basic attribute of each person. This is consistent with the importance of
   a. gender identity.
   b. gender consistency.
   c. sex typing.
   d. gender orientation.

2. Discouraging specific behaviors on the basis of gender is
   a. done by children only.
   b. done by parents only.
   c. done by parents and children.
   d. unrelated to cultural or social factors.

3. Masculinity and femininity appear to be
   a. on the opposite ends of a single dimension.
   b. two separate dimensions.
   c. inversely related to each other.
   d. part of a larger dimension.

4. Suppose Samuel has high scores on the masculinity and femininity scales of the BSRI. As such, he would be classified as
   a. reverse-typed.
   b. sex-typed.
   c. undifferentiated.
   d. androgynous.

5. The *most* accurate definition for gender-role identification is
   a. the degree to which an individual identifies with the gender stereotypes of his or her culture.
   b. whether one believes that men should be dominant and women should be passive regardless of culture.
   c. the average number of times per day that individuals encourage others to act according to their gender roles.
   d. the degree to which an individual believes that it is important to encourage gender roles and stereotypes.

6. Masculinity has been found to be particularly advantageous in ____ cultures.
   a. European
   b. African
   c. Asian
   d. Arab

7. Depression is often associated with
   a. hypermasculinity or hyperfemininity.
   b. traditional masculinity.
   c. androgyny.
   d. feminine role identification.

8. All of the following provide indications that gender stereotypes are fading away, *except*
   a. select contemporary motion pictures.
   b. certain children's books.
   c. the Judeo-Christian tradition.
   d. recent advertisements.

9. High levels of testosterone are believed to show special advantages in selecting a mate for
   a. men only.
   b. women only.
   c. men and women.
   d. neither men nor women.

10. Among the following individuals, the person who is *most* likely to be concerned about their weight would be a(n)
   a. lesbian.
   b. male.
   c. Asian woman.
   d. American woman.

Comprehensive Test
(NOTE: Items 1-15 are multiple-choice questions and items 16-23 are true-false questions.)

1. The ____ effect refers to the finding that information about the self is more readily processed and remembered than other information.
   a. self-efficacy
   b. self-focusing
   c. self-monitoring
   d. self-reference

2. Those who are most vulnerable to feedback indicating that they lack the necessary skills to enter their chosen profession are those who have
   a. a complex view of their possible selves.
   b. a limited number of possible future selves.
   c. possible selves that are unrealistically grounded.
   d. cultural taboos about thinking too much about the future.

3. One's ____ is measured in terms of a self-evaluation made along a positive-negative dimension.
   a. self-esteem
   b. self-concept
   c. self-schema
   d. self-monitoring

4. A downward comparison with someone who is very close to oneself
   a. raises self-esteem.
   b. doesn't influence self-esteem.
   c. produces a contrast effect.
   d. has a negative effect on self-esteem.

5. A very competent person with unrealistically negative self-esteem would exhibit
   a. evaluative-integrated self-organization.
   b. compartmentalized self-esteem.
   c. variable self-esteem.
   d. paradoxical self-esteem.

6. Persons who tailor their behavior to specific situations and audiences are said to be
   a. low in self-efficacy.
   b. high in self-efficacy.
   c. low in self-monitoring.
   d. high in self-monitoring.

7. Sex is to gender as
   a. men are to women.
   b. physical act is to biological reality.
   c. biology is to psychology.
   d. androgyny is to undifferentiated.

8. Between the ages of four and seven, children acquire the principles of ____, which means that they realize that gender is a basic attribute of a person that remains constant over time.
   a. gender consistency
   b. sex typing
   c. gender identity
   d. gender-role identification

9. Which of the following persons would be classified as androgynous?
   a. A person with high scores on the masculine and feminine scales of the BSRI.
   b. A person with low scores on the masculine and feminine scales of the BSRI.
   c. A man who scores high on the feminine scale but low on the masculine scale of the BSRI.
   d. A woman who scores high on the feminine scale but low on the masculine scale of the BSRI.

10. ____ involves an extreme gender-role identification with the female role.
    a. The traditional female role
    b. Androgyny
    c. Hyperfemininity
    d. Undifferentiated behavior

11. High levels of estrogen are associated with
    a. passivity.
    b. depression.
    c. heightened concern over weight.
    d. behavioral effects that are still widely unknown.

12. An example of the behavioral effects of high self-efficacy would be
    a. being less successful as a professor in terms of completing research projects.
    b. having less endurance in a challenging, physical exercise workout.
    c. falling short of one's own expectancies regarding performance.
    d. becoming a more efficient and effective physician.

13. Which of the following is *not* considered to be a sexual self-schema?
    a. open/direct
    b. sensual/physical
    c. romantic/passionate
    d. embarrassed/conservative

14. A therapeutic technique in which an individual is gradually taught to relax in the presence of a fear-producing stimuli, such as snakes, and in doing so gain an increased sense of self-efficacy is called
    a. social skills training.
    b. biofeedback.
    c. desensitization.
    d. flooding.

15. Only humans show ____ self-awareness.
    a. meaningful
    b. symbolic
    c. objective
    d. subjective

16. There does *not* appear to be a difference between Americans and Japanese individuals in terms of how frequently they show self-enhancement and self-criticism.

17. The self-reference effect helps to explain why you likely would pay particular attention to a person who has the same last name as yours.

18. An athlete who identifies strongly and exclusively with the role of an athlete will probably be more upset by an athletic injury than an athlete with a variety of future selves.

19. A high self-monitor tends to regulate his or her behavior on the basis of internal factors, such as values, beliefs, and attitudes.

20. The terms, "sex" and "gender," have identical meanings.

21. While a person can have either masculine or feminine characteristics, it is impossible to have both.

22. Hypermasculinity is typically conceptualized as the "ideal" gender-role identification for a male.

23. Men and women show an equal level of concern over the salary for a particular job.

When You Have Finished . . .

TOP TEN REASONS WHY THE STUDY OF THE SELF AND GENDER HAS GREAT RELEVANCE FOR *YOUR* LIFE

1. As trite as it may sound, the person who knows you the best is *yourself*. As such, we should all be aware and reflective of the components of our unique identities.

2. We live in a world where strong stereotypes about gender abound. By being more aware of these stereotypes, perhaps we may someday be able to live in a world where men and women are truly recognized and valued as a function to their abilities—and not by their sex.

3. Since very low and even very high levels of self-esteem can be harmful to our mental health and well-being, we should take an interest in having a fairly positive evaluation of our own worth.

4. By understanding the nature of sex differences, men and women may be in a better position to successfully contend with any conflict emanating from such differences.

5. By understanding your own gender identity, you can avoid potential problems that may occur as a result of such characteristics.

Let's revisit point #2. Pick a day to focus on any gender stereotypes that you observe, whether these are from media sources (e.g., television, magazine ads, roadside billboards), personal interactions or observations involving yourself or others, or from other sources. Try to note the occurrence and prevalence of such stereotypes and also note instances where you found examples of behavior that was inconsistent or contrary to such stereotypes.

Short Answer/Essay Questions

1. **Self-Concept**
   Compare and contrast the similarities and differences between men and women in terms of their sexual self-concepts.

2. **Social Comparisons**
   Suppose you make an upward social comparison with a stranger, a member of your in-group, and a close friend. Explain what the consequences of each of these comparisons will likely be—and why.

3. **Aspects of Self-Functioning**
   Janet tends to act and says things that are consistent with the actions and attitudes of those around her. Given this information, what characteristic is Janet displaying?

4. **Gender-Role Behavior**
   Discuss the different labels that a person may have as a consequence of completing the Bem Sex Role Inventory.

5. **Differences Between Men and Women**
   Consider the main differing self-perceptions of men and women.

6 PREJUDICE: ITS CAUSES, EFFECTS, AND CURES

Before you read . . .

This chapter addresses the very serious and important issue of prejudice in terms of why it happens, its effects, and how to prevent it. First, your text considers the general nature of prejudice and explains how it differs from discrimination. Afterward, a thorough overview regarding the origins of prejudice is presented. As you might expect, prejudice is derived from a variety of sources, such as social learning, intergroup conflict, social categorizations, stereotypes, illusory correlations, and out-group homogeneity. In this chapter, you'll have a good understanding as to why each of these sources may contribute to prejudice. Your text also offers an encouraging perspective as to why prejudice is *not* inevitable. You'll consider the many ways to reduce prejudice, such as learning techniques, direct intergroup contact, recategorization, cognitive interventions, and social influence. A discussion of how targets of prejudice cope and react to bigotry is also discussed. This chapter concludes with a discussion of the complex, though disturbing, issue of sexism. Interestingly enough, both men and women can shown prejudice based on gender. You'll also reviews the cognitive bases of sexism and how this has especially negative consequences for women in the workplace.

Chapter Objectives

After reading this chapter, you should be able to:

- Explain how schemas and negative emotions provide the basic foundations for prejudice.

- State the two basic reasons for why prejudice persists.

- Contrast the key difference between prejudice and discrimination.

- Understand how modern racism operates in contrast to "old-fashioned" racism.

- Describe how racial attitudes have been measured as a function of the "bogus pipeline" and the "bona fide pipeline."

- Consider why tokenism exists and its implications.

- Explain how realistic conflict theory helps to understand the origins of prejudice.

103

- Discuss the general methods and findings of the famous "Robber's Cave" study and why it is relevant to the study of prejudice.

- Contrast historical and contemporary social psychological views of whether poor economic conditions foster prejudice.

- Discuss how the social learning view of prejudice affects how a person develops attitudes about other racial or ethnic groups.

- Understand the nature and effects of social categorization and, in doing so, highlight the relevance of the ultimate attribution error and social identity theory.

- Offer a basic overview of what stereotypes are and how they operate.

- Compare and contrast how illusory correlations, in-group differentiation, and the illusion of out-group homogeneity all relate to the development of prejudice.

- Explain how the contact hypothesis and the extended contact hypothesis differ in terms of their predictions for how we can reduce prejudice.

- Consider how recategorizations, cognitive interventions, and social influence can all be used to reduce prejudice.

- Understand how individuals cope with prejudice.

- Explain how hostile and benevolent sexism function.

- Discuss how gender stereotypes and differential respect often provide the foundation for the cognitive bases of sexism.

- Understand why subtle forms of discrimination—particularly in the workplace—may still exist and, in doing so, explain what is meant by a "glass ceiling."

As you read . . .

Prejudice	Discrimination	Schemas
Stereotypes	Hate crimes	Modern racism
Explicit vs. implicit Attitudes	Bogus vs. bona fide pipeline	Tokenism
Realistic conflict theory	Superordinate goals	Social learning view
Social categorization	In- vs. out-group	Ultimate attribution error
Social identity theory	Illusory correlations	In-group differentiation
Illusion of out-group homogeneity	Appearance prejudice	Contact vs. extended contact hypotheses
Recategorization	Common in-group identity model	Category-driven processing
Stereotype threat	Sexism	Hostile vs. benevolent sexism
Gender stereotypes	Differential respect	Glass ceiling

Prejudice and Discrimination: Their Nature and Origins

➤ Prejudice: The Face of Intolerance

1. What is prejudice and how does it differ from discrimination? Also, note the role of schemas and emotions in terms of prejudicial attitudes.

➤ Prejudice: Why It Persists

1. Identify the two main reasons why prejudice persists.

➤ Discrimination: Prejudice in Action

1. Provide three recent examples of well-known hate crimes in the United States.

2. How does "modern racism" differ from "old-fashioned racism?"

3. Compare and contrast the research methodology associated with the "bogus pipeline" versus the "bona fide pipeline." What, precisely, are these measuring?

4. What is "tokenism?" Explain the consequences and impact of tokenism.

The Origins of Prejudice: Contrasting Perspectives

➤ Direct Intergroup Conflict: Competition as a Source of Prejudice

1. Why does prejudice occur according to realistic conflict theory?

2. The hatred shown by Osama bin Laden and his followers reveal an interesting aspect of realistic conflict theory. What is that aspect?

3. Summarize the methods employed by Sherif and colleagues (1961) in the famous "Robber's Cave" study. What did this study reveal about why prejudice occurs—and how we can reduce it? Also, what were some of the limitations of this classic study?

> ## Social Psychology: Thirty Years of Progress...Hard Economic Times and Violence Against Minority Groups: From Lynchings in the South to Hate Crimes in New York

1. Compare and contrast how social psychologists believed difficult economic times affected prejudice and violence against minorities in the 1940s (Then) versus the more current views on this topic (Now).

        Then   Now

➢ Early Experience: The Role of Social Learning

1. Evaluate the veracity of each of the following statements. If you believe the statement is *false*, then modify the *italicized* word in order to make the statement *true*.

    a.) According to the *social learning view*, prejudice is the end result of acquired negative attitudes from parents or friends that are rewarded in some way.

    b.) For white college students, concern with acting in a prejudiced manner tends to be positively related to pleasant interactions with blacks in *high school*.

    c.) Historically, minorities were cast in *low-status or comic roles* in the television and movies.

➢ Social Categorization: The Us-versus-Them Effect and the "Ultimate" Attribution Error

1. The tendency to divide the social world into two separate categories is known as _____

    _____; these two categories are the _____ and the _____

    _____. Sometimes, this reality often leads to the ultimate attribution error which is

    _____

    _____

    _____. This type of social categorization can lead to prejudice through social identity theory,

    which is _____.

    However, this tactic can succeed only to the extent that _____

    _____. Because all

    individuals are subject to the same tendencies, the final result is inevitable: _____

    _____.

➢ **Cognitive Sources of Prejudice: Stereotypes, Explicit, and Implicit**

1. In your own words, what is a "stereotype?" What do we do with information that's inconsistent with our stereotypes? Also, why might implicit stereotypes be a better predictor of subtle expressions of bias than explicit measures obtained through attitude questionnaires?

➢ **Other Cognitive Mechanisms in Prejudice: Illusory Correlations and Out-group Homogeneity**

1. White Americans tend to overestimate crime rates among African-American males. How is this an example of an illusory correlation?

2. Why would the statement, "You know what they're like; they're all the same," be an example of prejudice?

3. Why do people tend to perceive members of other groups as more homogeneous than members of our own group?

> ➤ **Beyond The Headlines: As Social Psychologists See It...Thin May Be "In," but in the United States, "Fat Is Where It's At": Combating Prejudice against Obese Persons**

1. What is appearance prejudice? Provide some examples of this form of prejudice. Is being thin universally viewed as attractive?

Why Prejudice Is *Not* Inevitable: Techniques for Countering Its Effects

---

> ➤ **Breaking the Cycle of Prejudice: On Learning *Not* to Hate**

1. Evaluate and summarize the evidence that bigots are made, not born.

> ## Direct Intergroup Contact: The Potential Benefits of Acquaintance

1. Define the contact hypothesis and state the three reasons why it truly can be effective in reducing prejudice. Also, note the conditions that must be met for it to work effectively.

2. What is the extended contact hypothesis and how does it differ from the contact hypothesis? State the four ways that it works to reduce prejudice.

> ## Recategorization: Redrawing the Boundary between "Us" and "Them"

1. Define the terms, "recategorization" and "common in-group identity model."

2. How can we induce people belonging to different groups to perceive each other as members of a single group?

> ## Cognitive Interventions: Can We Learn to Just Say "No" to Stereotypes?

1. How can we reduce the impact of stereotypes as a means of reducing prejudice and discrimination?

> ## Social Influence as a Means of Reducing Prejudice

1. If bigoted persons can be induced to believe that their prejudiced views are out of line with those of

most persons, especially _____, they

may well _____.

➢ **Coping with Prejudice: How Targets React to Bigotry**

1. Summarize the findings of Clark and Clark's (1947) well-known study of how white and black children responded to white and black dolls.

2. What is meant by "stereotype threat?" Describe at least one study that illustrates this phenomenon.

3. Compare and contrast the racial attitudes of blacks with those of whites.

Prejudice Based on Gender: Its Nature and Effects

➢ **Hostile and Benevolent Sexism: The Two Faces of Prejudice Based on Gender**

1. What is "sexism?" Contrast hostile sexism with benevolent sexism. Can women hold sexist views?

> ## The Cognitive Bases of Sexism: Gender Stereotypes and Differential Respect

1. Define the term, "gender stereotypes." Provide some examples of such stereotypes. Are these stereotypes accurate?

2. What is differential respect? Why do men *and* women express higher respect for men?

> ## Discrimination against Females: Subtle but Often Deadly

1. Identify how women have overcome certain forms of discrimination (for the most part) and yet, still experience certain disadvantages in many societies.

2. For each of the following descriptions, place an "X" to the left of the item if it tends to be associated with attitudes and behaviors expressed by most women.

____ Holding lower expectations about one's career

____ Feeling outraged over lower salaries for women than men

____ Comparing themselves with men and women

____ Expressing lower self-confidence than men in achievement-related situations

____ Using self-promoting strategies

3. How do people tend to react to women in positions of authority? Do they hold them in equally high regard as men?

4. What is a "glass ceiling?" Does it really exist? If so, why does it occur?

Thinking about The Aftermath of the September 11, 2001 Attacks and Prejudice

Another tragedy of the September eleventh disaster is that it revealed that prejudice is alive and well in our world. After all, the al-Qaeda terrorists who flew planes into the World Trade Center and Pentagon apparently held very strong anti-American sentiments. In the wake of these attacks, there have been some very unfortunate anti-Arab hate crimes in the United States. And, relatedly, in the wake of the growing Middle East crisis, there have been some rather disturbing anti-Semitic sentiments and acts occurring in various pockets in the world. Given what you now know about the social psychology of prejudice, how can we quell these hateful feelings?

After you read . . . Practice Tests

Practice Test 1

1. Prejudice is a phenomenon that affects
   a. minorities only.
   b. either those who hold racist views and the targets of racism.
   c. virtually everyone at some time or another.
   d. American society only.

2. Attitude is to behavior as
   a. discrimination is to prejudice.
   b. prejudice is to discrimination.
   c. prejudice is to schema.
   d. discrimination is to schema.

3. The two key reasons why prejudice persists are that it
   a. allows prejudiced persons to bolster their own self-image and it saves cognitive effort.
   b. saves cognitive effort and it enhances one's social status.
   c. provides an emotional outlet for aggressive tendencies and it is associated with reproductive success.
   d. minimizes one's life problems and it causes us to be more respected in the eyes of the prejudice target.

4. Dramatic instances of hate crimes
   a. rarely occur nowadays in the United States.
   b. are exploited and overemphasized by the media.
   c. continue to occur with disturbing frequency.
   d. appear to increase during harsh economic conditions.

5. Even though Chuck rarely discusses his views on race, he confesses to his friend that "people of color are given too many benefits in society." Chuck's views illustrate
   a. old-fashioned racism.
   b. modern racism.
   c. the bogus pipeline.
   d. the bona fide pipeline.

6. The bogus pipeline is to the bona fide pipeline as
   a. old-fashioned racism is to modern racism.
   b. modern racism is to old-fashioned racism.
   c. implicit is to explicit.
   d. explicit is to implicit.

7. Suppose Juanita discovers that she primarily was hired by a company because she is a Hispanic female. Upon learning this news, she will likely
   a. feel a bit troubled, but simply grateful for her job.
   b. realize that such hiring practices are the norm for most organizations.
   c. exhibit lowered self-esteem and confidence.
   d. feel greater motivation to showcase her talents.

8. According to realistic conflict theory, the main source of prejudice stems from
   a. a lack of communication.
   b. competition over valued resources.
   c. a need to enhance one's self-esteem.
   d. learned experiences.

9. Sherif's famous "Robber's Cave" study shows that competition can
   a. lead to violent conflict.
   b. promote healthy social interactions.
   c. decrease prejudice.
   d. be destructive only if it is not direct.

10. All of the following are shortcomings or limitations of the "Robber's Cave" study, *except*
    a. the study took place over a limited amount of time.
    b. all of the participants were boys.
    c. the study failed to yield concrete solutions as how to reduce prejudice.
    d. the participants had a fairly homogeneous background.

Practice Test 2

1. How do the results from recent research, in contrast to older research, differ (if at all) in terms of whether there is a relationship between economic hardship and racially motivated violence?
    a. The older research revealed a positive correlation between these two variables, whereas the recent research reveals a negative relationship.
    b. The older research revealed no relationship between these two variables, whereas the recent research showed a positive correlation.
    c. The older research revealed a positive correlation between these two variables, whereas the recent research has shown no stable relationship.
    d. Both the older and more recent research has consistently shown a positive correlation between these two variables.

2. Implicit racial attitudes appear to be related to positive interactions with blacks during
    a. preschool.
    b. elementary school.
    c. high school.
    d. college.

3. Nowadays, media portrayals of minorities are
    a. fairly infrequent.
    b. consistent with low-status or comic roles.
    c. overwhelmingly positive.
    d. shown in a somewhat more favorable manner than in the past.

4. Social categorization refers to the notion that people typically form two distinct groups known as
    a. in-groups and out-groups.
    b. we-groups and other-groups.
    c. us-groups and them-groups.
    d. friendly-groups and hostile groups.

5. Suppose Jason, an Italian-American, says "Italian-Americans tend to be hard working—but I just don't see that work ethic in other ethnic groups." His statement would be consistent with
    a. social identity theory.
    b. an illusory correlation.
    c. the fundamental attribution error.
    d. the ultimate attribution error.

6. Consistent with social identity theory, the key reason individuals identify with specific social groups is to
   a. denigrate members of other groups.
   b. enhance the self-esteem of the individual in question.
   c. highlight one's pride with respect to his or her social group.
   d. enhance one's self-understanding.

7. Which of the following statements about stereotypes is *false*?
   a. When we become aware about inconsistent information regarding our stereotypes, we tend to no longer have that stereotype.
   b. Stereotypes are cognitive frameworks that strongly influence the processing of incoming social information.
   c. Stereotypes have been conceptualized as inferential prisons.
   d. A stereotype does not necessarily have an obvious negative connotation.

8. Suppose an individual is told that there are one thousand members of Group A and one hundred members of Group B; moreover, one hundred members of Group A were arrested by the police last year and that ten members from Group B were arrested during the same time period. For which group will this individual *most* likely have a less favorable opinion?
   a. Group A
   b. Group B
   c. Both groups will probably be evaluated in a similar fashion.
   d. Most individuals will be reluctant to rate the groups until they have further information about them.

9. The mirror image of the illusion of out-group homogeneity effect is called
   a. an illusory correlation.
   b. the illusion of in-group heterogeneity.
   c. in-group differentiation.
   d. the ultimate attribution error.

10. Prejudice against persons who aren't considered attractive in their society is known as ____ prejudice.
    a. fat
    b. weight-related
    c. appearance
    d. physical beauty-based

Practice Test 3

1. Currently, the vast majority of social psychologists tend to believe that prejudice is
   a. linked to genetic factors.
   b. learned from parents only.
   c. learned from a variety of social influences.
   d. caused by an interaction of genetic and environmental factors.

2. The key difference between the extended contact hypothesis and the contact hypothesis is that
   a. the extended contact hypothesis states that individuals must have far more contact with members of different groups in order to reduce prejudice than the contact hypothesis initially stated.
   b. the contact hypothesis is most effective in promoting acquaintances, whereas the extended contact hypothesis suggests how to build close friendships.
   c. the extended contact hypothesis lays out a variety of conditions that must be present for prejudice to be reduced, whereas the contact hypothesis does not do so.
   d. unlike the contact hypothesis, the extended contact hypothesis suggests that simply knowing that members of one's own group have formed close friendships with members of an out-group can reduce prejudice.

3. The common in-group identity model suggests that when individuals belonging to different social groups come to view themselves as members of _____, their attitudes toward each other become more positive.
   a. two separate but equal groups
   b. a single social entity
   c. two distinct groups
   d. as members of a variety of sub-groups within the two groups

4. Suppose Jim is trying to change Xavier's prejudiced views by convincing him that his views are out of line with most persons. Will such a technique decrease Xavier's prejudice?
   a. Yes. This technique has been shown to universally alter prejudicial thinking.
   b. Possibly. This technique has been shown to be decrease prejudice—particularly if the bigoted person is convincing that someone he or she admires or respects doesn't approve of such views.
   c. No. This technique typically backfires and causes prejudiced persons to solidify their prejudiced views.
   d. At the current time, there is not enough research evidence to answer this question.

5. Stereotype threat refers to
   a. a concern that minorities will be evaluated in terms of stereotypes relating to their minority status.
   b. the notion that individuals are more likely to use stereotypes under threatening conditions.
   c. a belief that stereotypes are caused, in part, when an individual's self-esteem is threatened.
   d. how individuals process information that is inconsistent with their stereotypes.

6. In terms of sexist views, women
   a. rarely, if ever, hold such sentiments.
   b. can hold such sentiments, but these are much milder than men's sexist views.
   c. sometimes hold such views—even more strongly than men.
   d. almost always hold such sentiments to some degree.

7. Janet strongly believes that women are truly necessary for men's happiness. Her views is consistent with
   a. old-fashioned sexism.
   b. hostile sexism.
   c. benevolent sexism.
   d. no form of sexism whatsoever.

8. Suppose Sally and Tim work at the same company where there is a female and male co-president. Given this information, which of the following statements is *most* accurate?
    a. Sally and Tim will probably show equal levels of respect for their co-presidents.
    b. Sally will show more respect for the female co-president, whereas Tim will show more respect for the male co-president.
    c. Sally will show more respect for the male co-president, whereas Tim will show more respect for the female co-president.
    d. Sally and Tim will probably show more respect for their male co-president.

9. A final barrier that prevents women, as a group, from reaching the top positions in many companies is known as a(n)
    a. artificial barrier.
    b. glass ceiling.
    c. brick wall.
    d. cement floor.

10. Women tend to have ____ salary expectations since they usually compare themselves with ____.
    a. high; other women
    b. low; other women
    c. high; men
    d. low; men

Comprehensive Test
(NOTE: Items 1-15 are multiple-choice questions and items 16-23 are true-false questions.)

1. Prejudice refers to
    a. any kind of bias or inclination toward anything or anyone that may be considered inherently irrational.
    b. positive attitudes of a special kind.
    c. an usually negative attitude toward the members of some social group.
    d. attitudes of the majority toward the minority.

2. In the famous "Robber's Cave" study by Sherif and colleagues
    a. interactions between groups were hostile even before the study began.
    b. antagonism between the groups was caused because of boxing matches forced on the boys by the experimenters.
    c. the boys began to identify with their groups early.
    d. the boys had trouble developing group identities.

3. When we conceptualize "us" versus "them,"
    a. the "us" component is viewed in highly favorable terms.
    b. the "them" component is viewed in neutral terms.
    c. the "us" and "them" components are seen as complementary in nature.
    d. the "us" and "them" components are seen as merely dissimilar in nature and not antagonistic.

4. Recategorization refers to a(n)
   a. technique for collapsing the boundaries between antagonistic groups by having them pursue common goals.
   b. way for groups to switch their identities.
   c. ineffective technique designed to reduce prejudice.
   d. process by which children acquire prejudiced views.

5. According to the social learning view of prejudice, which of the following factors is *least* likely to cause the development of prejudiced views?
   a. sex role training
   b. inborn social tendencies
   c. parents and friends
   d. sociopolitical factors

6. Relative to men, women tend to be
   a. more ambitious.
   b. more concerned about money.
   c. less creative.
   d. less confident.

7. Tokenism refers to
   a. refusing to accept even a token gesture of friendship from an object of prejudice.
   b. being occasionally unfriendly to objects of prejudice.
   c. passing out to "tokens," such as small rewards or praise, to others who take a stand against discrimination.
   d. hiring a person solely on the basis of his or her racial or ethnic group membership and not his or her qualifications.

8. The bona fide pipeline makes use of _____ in order to study implicit racial attitudes.
   a. deception
   b. priming
   c. attributional biases
   d. one's self-concept

9. The hatred shown by Osama bin Laden and his supporters suggests that competition _____ real or direct to cause prejudice.
   a. must be
   b. must not be
   c. does not necessarily have to be
   d. must have religious overtones that are

10. Superordinate goals are ones that are
    a. desired by two separate groups.
    b. unpleasant for two separate goals.
    c. desired by one group and undesired by the other.
    d. tend to promote further disagreements between groups.

11. A possible reason for why Hovland and Sears (1940) found a significant positive relationship between harsh economic conditions and the incidence of racially motivated violence could be due to the fact that
    a. they apparently falsified their data.
    b. at that time, it was a very unsettled period for the Northeastern part of the United States.
    c. at that time, many political leaders blamed African-Americans for economic hardships.
    d. frustration always produces aggression.

12. Illusory correlations operate on the premise that
    a. individuals typically do not understand statistics.
    b. infrequent events are distinctive.
    c. people tend to perceive members of out-groups to be fairly similar to one another.
    d. our views are greatly influenced by our parents and peers.

13. Information that is inconsistent with one's stereotype tends to
    a. change the individual's stereotype.
    b. make one's stereotype stronger.
    c. be changed in ways that allow it to be consistent with the stereotype.
    d. simply be forgotten.

14. Prejudiced people are
    a. fortunately rare.
    b. made, not born.
    c. more blatant in their expressions than they used to be.
    d. an inevitable consequence of a diverse society.

15. Gender stereotypes typically occur for ____ and tend to be ____ in nature.
    a. women only; negative
    b. men or women; negative
    c. women only; positive or negative
    d. men or women; positive or negative

16. The devastating September 11, 2001 attacks on the World Trade Center and the Pentagon were largely caused by extreme prejudice.

17. Blatant forms of prejudice and discrimination have increased over the past few decades.

18. The boys in the famous Robber's Cave study came together once they received group therapy.

19. The social learning view of prejudice suggests that children can learn negative attitudes toward various groups from their parents.

20. Suppose George harbors racist views against African-Americans. When he hears a news report about an African-American who committed a crime, he feels that this provides further "proof" of his prejudiced views. This example illustrates an illusory correlation.

21. There is much support for the notion that hard economic times inevitably causes prejudice.

22. A key reason why women sometime face advancement problems in the workplace is that they often do *not* exhibit self-confidence or high expectations for themselves.

23. Women leaders tend to rated highly by other women.

When You Have Finished . . .

TOP TEN REASONS WHY THE STUDY OF PREJUDICE HAS GREAT RELEVANCE FOR *YOUR* LIFE

1. Since we know the damaging effects of prejudice, we should all be encouraged to prevent it as best as possible.

2. Since all of us at some time may be victims of prejudice, we need to be mindful of why this occurs and how we can cope with it.

3. We need to be aware of how sexism operates—particularly in the workplace—so that men *and* women will be evaluated as a function of their abilities.

4. Tragically, we all saw how extreme prejudice can affect all of our lives on September 11, 2001.

5. We need to be aware that prejudice does *not* have to exist merely as a function of race or gender. Your text highlights that prejudice can take many forms—such as prejudice against obese persons.

Let's reconsider point #2. Think back to when you may have been a victim of prejudice. What were the circumstances and how did you deal with it? Looking back at the situation, do you feel that you would have handled it differently now? If so, how?

Short Answer/Essay Questions

1. **Prejudice and Discrimination**
    Explain why the terms, "prejudice" and "discrimination," are NOT interchangeable.

2. **Realistic Conflict Theory**
   Briefly outline the main points of realistic conflict theory and note how it explains the hatred expressed by Osama bin Laden and his followers.

3. **Cognitive Mechanisms in Prejudice**
   Why do people tend to perceive members of other groups as more homogenous than members of our own groups?

4. **Coping with Prejudice**
   Define the stereotype threat and provide empirical evidence for its adverse effects.

5. **Sexism**
   Ida feels that women are superior to men in many ways in that they have better taste and more virtues. Would Ida's attitudes be indicative of sexism? If so, what kind of sexism?

<table>
<tr><td>

7

</td><td>

INTERPERSONAL ATTRACTION: MEETING, LIKING, BECOMING ACQUAINTED

</td></tr>
</table>

Before you read . . .

This chapter outlines interpersonal attraction by focusing on the early stages of how we become acquainted with someone and may grow to like him or her. Did you that some of the earliest phases of attraction may be related to such seemingly mundane things as how physically close you are located to a person? Your general emotions or affect can also greatly influence how you feel about a person. This chapter also makes the interesting point that there are individual differences and situational cues that are linked to our need to affiliate—and this also greatly influences how we become acquainted with others. Have you ever wondered which of these two famous sayings, "birds of a feather flock together" or "opposites attract," is accurate with respect to interpersonal attraction? Well, social psychologists believe that the former saying is, more the most part, quite correct. A very thorough consideration of how and why similarity affects attraction is discussed. This chapter also helps to serve as an introduction of the next chapter, which focuses on the study of close relationships.

Chapter Objectives

After reading this chapter, you should be able to:

- Provide an overview of the four key factors that need to be operating before individuals progress to the final stage of interpersonal attraction.

- Understand how proximity and repeated exposure can influence attraction (for better and sometimes worse).

- State the two most important characteristics of affect and note how emotions can influence attraction.

- Describe the need for affiliation, including its key characteristics and modes of expression.

- Consider how and why people evaluate others on the basis of physical attractiveness—particularly from an evolutionary perspective. Offer an overview of the key sex differences in terms of how men and women evaluate attractiveness

- Note the key features associated with physical attractiveness (regardless of one's sex).

127

- Consider the degree to which certain stereotypes about physical attractiveness are accurate.

- Understand the role that similarity plays in attraction.

- Highlight the key predictions of balance theory.

- Explain the repulsion hypothesis and how it is viewed by most contemporary social psychologists.

- Conceptualize the overall themes of interpersonal attraction with particular emphasis on the role of the affect-centered model of attraction.

As you read . . .

Remember this! Below are a list of some of the key terms and concepts from this chapter. Make flashcards in order to enhance your recall ability of these terms. Refer to the definitions that are either in boldface or in the margins of this chapter for help. Be advised that you may also want to include additional terms from this chapter as you deem necessary.

Interpersonal attraction	Proximity	Repeated exposure
Affect and its characteristics	(In)direct effects of emotion	Need for affiliation
Explicit vs. implicit motives	Needs for positive stimulation, social support, attention, and social comparison	Physical attractiveness
Appearance anxiety	"Average" attractiveness	Contrast effect
The "similarity hypothesis"	Attitude similarity	Proportion of similar attitudes
Balance theory and its three main states	The repulsion hypothesis	False consensus effect
Genocide and evolution	The slime effect	The affect-centered model of attraction

5. Identify at least one biological and one social/cultural reason why the evolutionary perspective on attractiveness may *not* be completely accurate.

6. Complete the chart below by listing facial features or characteristics that are generally viewed as attractive for men only, women only, and both men and women.

Men only	Women only	Both men and women

7. For each of the following pairs, circle the characteristic that most people will typically like:

   a.) A person who is underweight vs. a person who is overweight.

   b.) Rapid eye blinking vs. slow eye blinking.

   c.) A firm handshake vs. a loose handshake.

   d.) An expression of anger vs. an expression of sadness.

   e.) A dominant male vs. a noncompetitive male.

   f.) The name, "Joshua," vs. the name, "Roscoe."

➢ Beyond the Headlines: As Social Psychologists See It...Do Looks and Style Influence Voters?

1. Your text presents the provocative view that a contributing factor to Al Gore's "defeat" (I place defeat in quotes because in some circles, many still believe he "won" the election) in the 2000 presidential race was the fact that he had a right part (as opposed to a left part) for his hair. In a race where the candidates were officially separated by 537 votes in the critical state of Florida, it seems that virtually *any* factor could've influenced the race. But still, to what degree do you feel that looks and style factored into that—or any—election? Do you think looks and style play too large a role in politics?

Moving toward Friendship: Similarity and Mutual Liking

➢ Similarity: Birds of a Feather Really Do Flock Together

1. Most laypersons are familiar with the contradictory sayings, "birds of a feather flock together" and "opposites attract." Which saying is correct? Why? Be sure to provide research evidence to support your claims.

2. Identify and define the three possible states as predicted by balance theory. What are the consequences of being in these states?

3. Are there evolutionary reasons for why genocide and war occurs? Evaluate the evidence.

➢ Social Psychology: Thirty Years of Progress: Similarity, Dissimilarity, or Both?

1. Compare and contrast how the repulsion hypothesis was initially conceptualized and shortly thereafter rejected (Then) and, more recently, how certain aspects of this hypothesis have been shown to contain a partial truth (Now).

    <u>Then</u>   <u>Now</u>

> ### Mutual Liking: Attraction toward Those Who Are Attracted to Us

1. Once two people discover that they're sufficiently similar to be able to move toward establishing a

   friendship, one additional step is crucial. That step is _____

   _____ .

2. When Person A and Person B interact, list all of the processes that are occurring according to the affect-centered model of attraction.

Thinking about The Aftermath of the September 11, 2001 Attacks and Interpersonal Attraction

Your text suggests that, consistent with an evolutionary psychological perspective, genocide and war may be an unfortunate by-product of evolution. With the September eleventh attacks as a backdrop for this question, do you agree with this perspective? Why?

After you read . . . Practice Tests

Practice Test 1

1. ____ signifies the final step or stage of interpersonal attraction.
   a. The need to affiliate
   b. Positive emotions
   c. Physical proximity
   d. Mutual liking

2. You would expect to have a ____ level of attraction for a superficial acquaintance.
   a. mild liking
   b. neutral
   c. mild disliking
   d. strong disliking

3. Another term for physical proximity is
   a. closeness.
   b. affiliation.
   c. similarity.
   d. physical attraction.

4. The underlying factor as to why proximity tends to promote liking is due to
   a. perceived similarity.
   b. repeated exposure.
   c. positive affect.
   d. personality differences.

5. Suppose Billy hears a song on the radio that he initially dislikes and continues to hear it played on the radio many additional times. The additional exposures to this song will likely cause him to
   a. increase his liking for the song.
   b. increase his dislike for the song.
   c. not change his attitudes about the song.
   d. reconsider his feelings about the song.

6. Suppose Sarah and Jon are two college students who live in a college dormitory designed for students who are Jewish or have interests in Jewish culture. They live right across the hall from each other and soon start dating each other. Given this information, which of the following statements is *most* accurate?
   a. Their proximity is causing attraction.
   b. Their attraction has caused their proximity.
   c. Their ethnicity has lead to their attraction and proximity.
   d. Their attraction is unrelated to their proximity or ethnicity.

7. The two key characteristics of affect are
   a. emotions and feelings.
   b. positive and negative.
   c. intensity and direction.
   d. degree and quality.

8. Positive and negative emotions are usually conceptualized as
   a. two separate and independent dimensions.
   b. opposite ends of the same dimension.
   c. being unable to experience positive and negative states at the same time.
   d. having an inverse relationship with each other.

9. Suppose Jill reacts harshly to a stranger while shopping at a store simply because she had a major fight with her boyfriend. This is an example of a(n) ____ effect of emotion on attraction, which is based on ____ conditioning.
   a. direct; classical
   b. indirect; classical
   c. direct; instrumental
   d. indirect; instrumental

10. When an individual interacts with a stigmatized person for the first time, he or she will likely experience all of the following, *except*
   a. increased blood pressure.
   b. a feeling of threat.
   c. diminished performance.
   d. information overload.

Practice Test 2

1. Affective influences on voters tend to be strongest when voters are
   a. politically uninformed.
   b. politically informed.
   c. not consciously motivated to evaluate the candidates.
   d. moderate in their political orientation.

2. Which of the following individuals illustrates the need for affiliation as a trait?
   a. Zeke, who is trying to comfort his neighbors after they experienced a major tornado.
   b. Sue, who tends to work in a very cooperative manner with her co-workers.
   c. Jeff, who after being diagnosed with cancer, decides to seek out support from other cancer patients.
   d. Mindy, who along with her fellow concert-goers, is dancing at a rock concert.

3. Our need for ____ pertains to the desire to obtain knowledge and reduce uncertainty.
   a. social support
   b. social comparison
   c. attention
   d. positive stimulation

4. Being independent and successful are two characteristics that are associated with attractiveness in
   a. men only.
   b. women only.
   c. men and women.
   d. neither men nor women.

5. An undue concern with one's looks is called
   a. appearance anxiety.
   b. physical attractiveness concerns.
   c. social anxiety.
   d. physical appearance phobia.

6. All of the following characteristics appear to be associated with attractiveness across most cultures, *except*
   a. adjustment.
   b. sexual warmth.
   c. intelligence.
   d. integrity.

7. An example of a stereotype based on appearance that is largely accurate is
   a. only physically unattractive individuals commit heinous deeds or crimes.
   b. kind and intelligent people tend to be physically unattractive.
   c. those who are most attractive are (correctly) believed to more popular and have greater interpersonal skills.
   d. non-existent—all of the stereotypes based on appearance are false.

8. From an evolutionary perspective, the point that men tend to place a greater premium on physical attractiveness and youth is due to
   a. a variety of societal and environmental influences.
   b. the point that most women realize that is superficial to make definitive judgments about a mate solely on the basis of their looks.
   c. women's common knowledge that relationships with extremely attractive men tend to end in failure.
   d. the fact that women have a limited period of their lives where they are fertile in contrast to men.

9. A possible limitation of the evolutionary perspective in terms of mate selection is that
   a. it overly emphasizes the importance of environmental factors.
   b. gay men often show an analogous preference for male partners in the same that heterosexual men have for female partners.
   c. even though this theory predicts that women should value a man's social status, research on this topic has confirmed otherwise.
   d. it fails to why certain characteristics of "attractiveness" should be associated with reproductive success.

10. Women with _____ are generally considered to be attractive.
    a. childlike but not mature features
    b. mature but not childlike features
    c. either childlike or mature features
    d. neither childlike nor mature features

Practice Test 3

1. Suppose Dr. Smith has collected pictures of ten women and intends to create composite images of them on her computer. Most individuals will likely find the *most* attractive face to be
   a. any single picture.
   b. a composite of half (or five) of the faces.
   c. a composite of all ten faces.
   d. debatable—based on this information, there likely will not be a general consensus.

2. Facial symmetry is associated with
   a. sexual promiscuity.
   b. general health.
   c. extremely masculine or feminine characteristics.
   d. physical unattractiveness.

3. Suppose Ryan has a thin, angular body shape. Consequently, people will likely judge him as being
   a. sad and sloppy.
   b. in good health, yet having few intellectual interests.
   c. intelligent and fearful.
   d. dynamic and rigid.

4. If a political candidate has a specific ethnic last name, then this is considered to be an
   a. overall net negative.
   b. overall net positive.
   c. overall net positive if it is popular within a given geographic area.
   d. overall net positive if the candidate is a male.

5. Physically attractive women have ____ weight and diet concerns with respect to less attractive women since ____.
   a. greater; physically attractive women tend to be more concerned with being thin.
   b. less; physically attractive women tend to be more concerned with being thin.
   c. the same; all women have an equal concern with being thin.
   d. less; less attractive women are trying harder to lose weight and diet.

6. Suppose you find out that your sister is having a baby and you are trying to offer her some advice about baby names. On the basis of research in this area, what advice should you offer?
   a. Be sure to select a name that is considered to be "trendy" at the time of the baby's birth.
   b. Just go with a name that sounds "right"—one's name really makes very little difference in terms of interpersonal perceptions.
   c. If she has a girl and wants to name her "Hillary," assure her that very few people would associate her in any way with Senator Hillary Rodham Clinton.
   d. Be aware that various male and female names are associated with specific positive and negative stereotypes.

7. The general idea that similarity fosters interpersonal attraction was first noted by scholars
   a. within the past few decades.
   b. during the 1920s.
   c. well over a century ago.
   d. well over two thousand years.

8. Suppose Phil and Jake discuss six issues and are in agreement on two of them. Their proportion of similar attitudes would be ____.
   a. 2
   b. .33
   c. .67
   d. 4

9. Suppose Carla and Heather dislike each other. As such, they are in a state of ____.
   a. balance
   b. imbalance
   c. unbalance
   d. nonbalance

10. The evolutionary perspective would likely predict that genocide and human animosity is ____ with this perspective since ____.
   a. consistent; we often have harsh reactions to dissimilarity.
   b. consistent; we realize that this behavior is a way to showcase our strengths.
   c. inconsistent; we understand that this is destructive to the human race.
   d. inconsistent; we perceive such behaviors to be incompatible with reproductive success.

Comprehensive Test

(NOTE: Items 1-15 are multiple-choice questions and items 16-23 are true-false questions.)

1. Subliminal repeated exposure has been shown to
   a. produce no change in liking for the exposed stimulus.
   b. cause subjects to dislike the exposed stimulus.
   c. increase liking for the exposed stimulus.
   d. produce recognition of the exposed stimulus, but no change in liking.

2. Moreland and Beach (1992) had female assistants attend a college class not at all, a few times, or several times. When members of the class rated the assistant for likeability, it was found that
   a. how often assistants attended class didn't affect likeability.
   b. assistants who attended a few times were rated more likeable.
   c. assistants who attended several times were rated more likeable.
   d. frequency of attendance wasn't important; the one significant factor was the assistants' attractiveness.

3. Consistent with research on proximity in the classroom, you would expect that
   a. people seated at the end of a row make more friends than those in the middle.
   b. when seating is alphabetical, friendships seldom form with people whose names begin with the same or a nearby letter.
   c. someone seated to your right or left is not likely to become your friend.
   d. changing seat assignments once or twice a semester results in each student having more acquaintances.

4. All of the following are considered attractive, *except*
   a. "childlike" features in women.
   b. "mature" features in women.
   c. an "average" face created by digitizing.
   d. an asymmetrical face.

5. Rosenbaum's repulsion hypothesis states that
   a. opposite views lead to attraction.
   b. we respond to physically unattractive individuals with rejection.
   c. we are most likely to terminate a romantic relationship when we are repulsed by our partner's behavior.
   d. we dislike a stranger who holds dissimilar attitudes than our own.

6. When two people like each other and agree , there is____; however, when two people like each other and disagree, there is ____.
   a. balance; imbalance
   b. balance; nonbalance
   c. nonbalance; imbalance
   d. imbalence; balance

7. Jim truly believes that "almost everyone agrees with me." Such a sentiment is consistent with the
   a. false consensus effect.
   b. need for affiliation.
   c. repulsion hypothesis.
   d. asymmetric reasoning effect.

8. The affect-centered model of attraction contains all of the following elements, *except*
   a. it is a conceptual framework pertaining to attraction.
   b. it assumes that negative emotions are more important than positive emotions.
   c. emotion can be aroused from a variety of sources.
   d. when two individuals interact, they are simultaneously reacting to and processing information about each other.

9. _____ refers to an attitude about another person.
   a. Interpersonal influence
   b. Interpersonal attraction
   c. Social cognition
   d. Person perception

10. Continued contact with a stigmatized person tends to _____ the threatening element of the interaction for an individual.
    a. increase
    b. decrease
    c. stabilize
    d. highlight

11. Ostracism during Internet chat room sessions
    a. produces negative emotions for the individual in question.
    b. has no effect on the individual, since he or she realizes that the interaction really isn't "real."
    c. only bothers an individual when he or she personally know the other individuals in the chat room.
    d. motivates the individual to find another chat room where he or she will likely receive responses from others.

12. The _____ of attractiveness stereotypes depends on which characteristics are valued by a particular culture.
    a. objective validity
    b. general nature
    c. specific content
    d. overall use

13. Given that females prefer males on the basis of their resources, particularly in cultures where women are less well educated, this offers support for _____ of attraction.
    a. the evolutionary theory (only)
    b. the culture-based theory (only)
    c. both the evolutionary and culture-based theories
    d. neither the evolutionary nor the culture-based theories

14. Suppose Jerry, after viewing pictures of extremely attractive women, finds his own girlfriend to be less attractive. Given this information, this could be explained by
    a. Jerry's dispositional tendencies.
    b. the fact that their relationship is troubled.
    c. the false consensus effect.
    d. the contrast effect.

15. The basic premise behind the "similarity hypothesis" is that
    a. similarity is merely correlation with attraction.
    b. similarity causes attraction.
    c. attraction causes similarity.
    d. either similarity or dissimilarity can promote attraction.

16. Repeated exposure typically increases our liking for a person or stimulus.

17. Katie, a newborn, will likely smile at a picture of her grandparents, even though she has never seen them before.

18. People tend to *not* show much agreement over the specific characteristics that are associated with attractiveness.

19. The repulsion hypothesis stipulates that attitude similarity causes decreased attraction.

20. Marcia and Fran are good friends, but they are in disagreement over a certain issue. As such, there is an imbalance with respect to their friendship.

21. Consistent with evolutionary theory, men and women place an equal value on a potential mate's physical appearance.

22. Charlie likes to spend time with others as much as possible. As such, he appears to have a need for acceptance.

23. Consistent with the affect-centered model of attraction, if you were in a bad mood while interacting with a particular person, then there is a strong likelihood that you will form a negative view of this person.

When You Have Finished . . .

TOP TEN REASONS WHY INTERPERSONAL ATTRACTION HAS GREAT RELEVANCE FOR *YOUR* LIFE

1. We are always meeting a new person on a regular basis and evaluating them: This is what interpersonal attraction is all about!

2. Given the overwhelmingly important of similarity in fostering interpersonal attraction, this information should help to give you a better understanding on the likelihood that you will become good friends with someone.

3. We can use some basic findings with respect to proximity and repeated exposure to either encourage or decrease the likelihood that we will make new friends.

4. By understanding the importance of affect in interpersonal attraction, we are better equipped to realize its effects when we are becoming acquainted with someone.

5. We should be mindful that—whether we like it or not—physical appearance and one's general style can often have a great impact on whether we like someone. By simply being aware of this information, we also can realize that interpersonal attraction may be greatly influenced by seemingly trivial or superficial factors.

Let me reflect on point #3 for a moment. Truth be told, my wife and I actually were "next door neighbors" in a dormitory during our freshman year in college. As with any relationship, there are many reasons why we shared a feeling of attraction for each other and eventually wed. However, I firmly believe that simply living next door to each other played a very important role in the earliest stages of our relationship. Can you think of individuals who became close friends—or even spouses—of yours after living or working in close proximity with them? If so, how did this come about?

Short Answer/Essay Questions

1. **Proximity and Repeated Exposure**
   Summarize how proximity and repeated exposure usually function in natural settings and discuss whether there is a causal relationship between these variables.

2. **The Need to Affiliate**
   Define what is meant by a person's need for affiliation and briefly outline the difference between how this need is shown as a function of traits and states.

3. **Physical Attractiveness**
   Briefly outline why physical attractiveness should matter from an evolutionary perspective.

4. **Balance Theory**
   John and Steve are good friends but they find themselves in some disagreement over a political issue that they are discussing. Consistent with balance theory, how would you describe the state of their relationship and how will John and Steve likely contend with this state?

5. **Similarity versus Dissimilarity: The Repulsion Hypothesis**
   State the repulsion hypothesis and evaluate its veracity.

8 CLOSE RELATIONSHIPS:
FAMILY, FRIENDS, LOVERS, AND SPOUSES

Before you read . . .

In the last chapter, we considered the initial stages of attraction. This chapter considers the nature of our well-established, ongoing close relationships. In particular, you'll quickly discover the important and defining role of interdependence in close relationships. Then this chapter discusses our earliest types of close relationships—those with our parents and siblings. In doing so, the increasing importance of attachment styles is fully considered. A consideration of how close friendships operate will also be featured. You'll also consider what life is like for lonely people who do *not* have any close, intimate relationships. Have you ever wondered just "what is this crazy little thing called *love*?" Well, we'll consider the nature of love and sexuality in romantic relationships. Then we consider the realities of married life. Have you ever wondered what is the "secret" of a happy marriage? Many of these so-called secrets will be revealed in the latter part of this chapter. You'll also consider why marriages sometimes fail and how people cope with a failing marriage or intimate romantic relationship.

Chapter Objectives

After reading this chapter, you should be able to:

- Understand the concept of interdependence and its relevance to close relationships.

- Outline some of the major characteristics of parent-child and sibling relationships.

- Consider the nature of close friendships and highlight how same-sex and opposite-sex friendships tend to function.

- Detail and contrast the three initial types of attachment outlined (in the study of parent/mother-infant interactions) with the four types offered by Bartholomew and colleagues.

- Consider why loneliness develops, its consequences, and ways to overcome it.

- Explain why and how a romantic relationship differs from a close friendship.

- Clarify how passionate love differs from unrequited and companionate love.

- Contrast the elements of Hendrick and Hendrick's (1986) love styles with that of Sternberg's (1986) triangular model of love.

- Outline how sexuality and sexual practices have differed over the course of the past several decades and discuss the implications of these changes.

- Discuss the importance and role of similarity, assumed similarity, individual differences, and sexual interactions in a marriage.

- Consider the benefits and challenges of marriage.

- Discuss how parenthood affects marriage and note how the prototype of the American family has been changing over the past few decades.

- Outline some of the common problems faced by married couples and helpful ways to deal with these issues.

- Discuss the behavioral options for those in a troubled marriage or intimate relationship.

As you read . . .

> **Remember this! Below are a list of some of the key terms and concepts from this chapter. Make flashcards in order to enhance your recall ability of these terms. Refer to the definitions that are either in boldface or in the margins of this chapter for help. Be advised that you may also want to include additional terms from this chapter as you deem necessary.**

Close relationships	Interdependence	Characteristics of parent-child and sibling relationships
Close friendships	Attachment style	Working models
Bowlby's three attachment styles	Interpersonal trust	Secure, fearful-avoidant, preoccupied, and dismissing attachment styles
Loneliness	Personal negativity and hopelessness	Cognitive therapy
Social skills training	Close friendships vs. romances	Belief in romantic destiny
Love	Passionate love	Unrequited love
Companionate love	Hendrick and Hendrick's six love styles	Sternberg's triangular model of love
Consummate love	Intimacy	Passion
Decision/commitment	Erotophilic vs. erotophobic	(Un)Restricted sociosexual orientation
Unwanted pregnancies/teenage pregnancy epidemic	Sexually transmitted diseases/HIV and AIDS	Assumed similarity

Narcissism	Cohabiting	Qualities of marital love and parenthood
Communal behavior	Causes of and solutions for marital problems	Exit, voice, neglect, and loyalty

---

Interdependent Relationships with Family and Friends versus Loneliness

---

➤ Family: The First Relationships

1. Identify and discuss the common factor included in all close relationships.

2. What's wrong here? Each of the following statements is *false*. Modify some aspect of each statement in order to make it *true*.

   a.) Infants are ready to interact with others at around two months of age.

   b.) The nature of parent-child interactions depends solely on the personality of the child.

   c.) Adolescents routinely report that they dislike their parents.

   d.) Mothers never report that they were closer to one of their grown children than to the others.

   e.) Siblings tend to be very close in early childhood, but then grow and stay apart.

➤ Relationships beyond the Family: Establishing a Close Friendship

1. Note the characteristics of a close friendship. Discuss the role of gender in friendships.

➤ Adult Relationships and Attachment Style

1. Name that attachment style! For each of the following hypothetical individuals, state their likely attachment style (based on the four attachment styles proposed by Bartholomew).

    a.) Jane, who says "my friends seldom live up to my expectations." _____

    b.) Bob, who feels that "most people don't like me." _____

    c.) Cindy, who says that she "falls in love easily." _____

    d.) Gabriel, who says that he "enjoys looking at himself in the mirror." _____

➤ Social Psychology...Thirty Years of Progress: The Importance of Adult Attachment Style in Interpersonal Behavior

1. Compare and contrast how social psychologists studied the issue of attachment style thirty years ago (Then) versus the more current views on this topic (Now).

    <u>Then</u>   <u>Now</u>

➤ Loneliness: Life without Close Relationships

1. In your own words, define "loneliness." Why does it occur and what are its consequences?

2. Is there any hope for lonely people to overcome their loneliness? If so, identify the ways by which they can overcome loneliness.

Romantic Relationships, Love, and Physical Intimacy

> ## Romance: Beyond Friendship

1. *She loves me, she loves me not...*Place a star next to each of the following statements *if* it is consistent with behavior that you'd expect to find in a romantic relationship.

   Expecting that one's partner be honest and loyal in a homosexual relationship.

   A preference for someone who will provide accurate feedback relevant to his or her self-concept.

   A relationship built on fantasy.

   A tendency for there to be a happy relationship when an individual matches his or her partner's ideals.

   A keen ability to predict how long their relationship will last.

> ## Beyond the Headlines: As Social Psychologists See It...Are Seven-Minute Dates the Solution?

1. Discuss the phenomena of "fast dating" and Internet contacts. Highlight the pros and cons of each. Would *you* partake in such behavior in order to find a mate?

➢ **What Is This Thing Called Love?**

1. *Crazy little thing called love…* There have been countless songs and poems about love—so, let's consider what social psychologists have said about this topic. Actually, let's evaluate the statements being said in the following hearts and denote the type of love being illustrated.

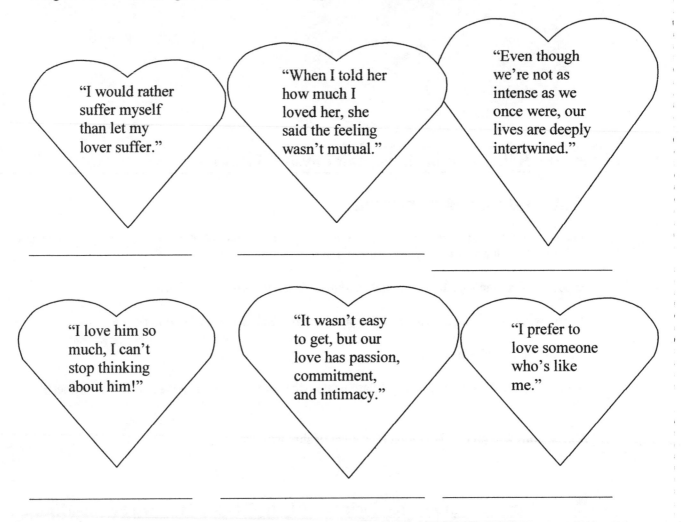

➢ **Sexuality in Romantic Relationships**

1. *Let's talk about sex*—well, specifically, sexuality in romantic relationships. Examine each of the following statements. Some will be true, some will not. If the statement is *not* true, then modify the word in *italics* in order to make it true.

    a.) Many college students *do not* view oral sex as "having sex."

    b.) In the 1950s, premarital sex was *fairly rare.*

c.) *Erotophilic* refers to extremely negative attitudes about sex.

d.) Those with a(n) *restricted* sociosexual orientation feel that a sexual relationship is only appropriate when accompanied by affected.

e.) A general concern for the issue of unwanted pregnancies first began in the *1960s*.

f.) Women who are sexually intimate with only one male partner *cannot* contract AIDS.

g.) The rate of overall growth of AIDS in the United States is about *ten* percent.

Marriage: The Ultimate Close Relationship

> ## Marital Success and Marital Satisfaction: Similarity, Assumed Similarity, Personality, and Sex

1. Complete the sentences below by filling in the blanks.

   a.) Couples who've been married for many years show _____ in their degree of similarity over time.

   b.) _____ refers to the point that spouses tend to assume greater similarity than is the case.

   c.) Marital success is _____ by whether a women uses her own surname or not.

   d.) A _____ feels superior to most people are lacks empathy for others.

   e.) The most sexually active couples are _____.

> ## Marital Love, Career, Parenthood, and the Changing Composition of Families

1. Is being married better than being single?

2. What type of love is essential for success in a marriage?

3. How do husbands and wives distribute work inside and outside the home?

4. How do husbands and wives respond to parenthood?

5. Is "married with children" the norm in the United States?

> ## Relationship Problems, Reactions to the Problems, and the Effects of Relationship Failure

1. Describe the possible problems that spouses may face. In doing so, discuss the role of communal behavior.

2. Outline helpful and hurtful ways to react to marital problems.

3. Outline the four possible ways to respond to a troubled relationship.

4. State the three factors that can enable a couple to reconcile a deteriorating relationship.

Thinking about The Aftermath of the September 11, 2001 Attacks and Close Relationships

In the time since the attacks, many individuals have tried to understand the mindset of a terrorist. To what degree do you think attachment style is a factor in determining the likelihood that one will become a terrorist? To put it another way, how likely do you believe a person with a secure attachment style (in particular) would become a terrorist?

After you read . . . Practice Tests

Practice Test 1

1. The common element to all close relationships is
   a. intimacy.
   b. sexual warmth.
   c. equity.
   d. interdependence.

2. Human infants are ready to interact with others
   a. from birth.
   b. at around their second week of life.
   c. at around their first month of life.
   d. between ages two to three months.

3. Adolescents typically respond to their parents
   a. with general contempt.
   b. with overwhelmingly positive feelings.
   c. by being less close and dependent on them than they were in childhood.
   d. with great fluctuations in emotion so that one moment they love them and the next they do not.

4. Boys appear to be at greatest risk for behavior problems if they
   a. have an aloof father.
   b. are an only child.
   c. only have a sister.
   d. have a high level of contact with their siblings and a rejecting, punitive mother.

5. Two key characteristics of close friendships is that the individuals tend to avoid
   a. self-disclosure and mutual support.
   b. bragging and lying.
   c. modesty and lying.
   d. doing varied activities and sensitivity.

6. In the earliest work on attachment, it was argued that there were _____ styles of attachment.
   a. two
   b. three
   c. four
   d. five

7. The two central cognitions that an infant and his or her caregiver develop pertain to
   a. self-esteem and interpersonal trust.
   b. empathy and sympathy.
   c. self-esteem and self-awareness.
   d. interpersonal warmth and interpersonal trust.

8. A significant negative effect associated with a secure attachment style is
    a. overly inflated self-esteem.
    b. a tendency to dominate others in relationships.
    c. putting others ill at ease.
    d. apparently nonexistent—at this time, there appears to be no negative effects associated with this attachment style.

9. Joyce has low self-esteem and generally holds negative views about others. As such, she'd likely be classified as having a _____ attachment style.
    a. fearful-avoidant
    b. dismissing
    c. secure
    d. preoccupied

10. If Jack, an infant, has a secure attachment with his parents, will he necessarily have a secure attachment with close others when he is an adult?
    a. Yes, he will definitely have a secure attachment as an adult.
    b. Not necessarily, there are many other factor that could affect his attachment style.
    c. No, there is evidence that individuals tend to develop an adult attachment style that is markedly different from that with their parents.
    d. Since researchers have not considered this issue at all, there is no way to evaluate this question.

Practice Test 2

1. Loneliness develops as a result of
    a. individual experiences only.
    b. cultural influences and individual experiences only.
    c. genetics and individual experiences.
    d. genetics, individual experiences, and cultural influences.

2. Extreme loneliness may culminate in
    a. feelings of personal negativity.
    b. a sense of complete hopelessness.
    c. a yearning to have friends.
    d. suicide.

3. A need for acceptance is particularly important and accurate feedback is *not* usually desired in a
    a. friendship.
    b. marriage.
    c. romantic relationship (at least at the beginning).
    d. parent-child relationship.

4. The Internet offers all of the following advantages pertaining to relationship development, *EXCEPT*
   a. increased anonymity.
   b. reduced importance of physical appearance.
   c. greater control over the time and place of interactions.
   d. increased pressure to make the first move in a relationship.

5. Experiences of unrequited love are particularly likely to occur for
   a. women.
   b. elderly individuals.
   c. those with an anxious-ambivalent attachment style.
   d. those with an avoidant attachment style.

6. _____ love is characteristic of those who are concerned with themselves and their own independence.
   a. Companionate
   b. Consummate
   c. Game-playing
   d. Logical

7. In Sternberg's triangular model of love, intimacy plus passion equals
   a. romantic love.
   b. infatuation.
   c. fatuous love.
   d. empty love.

8. Nowadays, _____ report having sexual intercourse for the first time on their wedding night _____.
   a. women; more frequently than they used to
   b. men and women; more frequently than they used to
   c. women; rarely
   d. men and women; rarely

9. Sam believes that a sexual relationship is acceptable only when accompanied by affection and tenderness. This view is consistent with a(n) _____.
   a. unrestricted sociosexual orientation
   b. restricted sociosexual orientation
   c. unrestricted psychosexual orientation.
   d. unrestricted psychosexual orientation.

10. A general, heightened awareness of the dangers of sexually transmitted diseases and unwanted pregnancies begun during the
   a. 1960s.
   b. 1970s.
   c. 1980s.
   d. 1990s.

Practice Test 3

1. The incidence of HIV infections in the United States is considerably higher among all of the following groups (compared with the national average), *except*
    a. women who are in their thirties.
    b. gay men.
    c. the poor.
    d. minority groups.

2. Similarity is to assumed similarity as
    a. correct is to incorrect.
    b. objective is to subjective.
    c. subjective is to objective.
    d. incorrect is to correct.

3. Joe feels superior to most other individuals, lacks empathy for others, and is sensitive to criticism. As such, he would be considered to be
    a. psychotic.
    b. a narcissist.
    c. high in neuroticism.
    d. suffering from social phobia.

4. ____ couples tend to share household chores in an equitable manner.
    a. African-American
    b. Latino
    c. Lesbian
    d. Cohabiting

5. As the number of children increases in a marriage, ____ report decreased satisfaction with the marriage.
    a. only men
    b. only women
    c. men and women
    d. neither men nor women

6. In the United States, the "married with children" household
    a. is the norm.
    b. was the norm until the 1990s.
    c. is quickly becoming the norm again.
    d. hasn't been the norm for several decades.

7. All of the following are possible sources of trouble in a long-term marriage, *except*
    a. growing costs of the relationship.
    b. changing in different directions as a couple.
    c. discovering that the actual similarity for the couple is different than their assumed similarity.
    d. expressing relationship problems in an agreeable way.

8. Suppose a couple decides to take a cross-country trip across America in the hope of making their relationship "less boring." This decision will likely
    a. have no effect on the quality of their relationship.
    b. enhance their relationship.
    c. worsen their relationship.
    d. promote negative affect.

9. Successful marriages tend to have all of the following characteristics, *except*
    a. lustful attraction.
    b. friendship.
    c. a consistent determination to create positive affect.
    d. social support.

10. About _____ of American children have divorced parents.
    a. one-quarter
    b. one-third
    c. one-half
    d. two-thirds

Comprehensive Test
(NOTE: Items 1-15 are multiple-choice questions and items 16-23 are true-false questions.)

1. Loneliness is
    a. feeling alone under any circumstance.
    b. any perception of solitary that is (in fact) valid.
    c. the unmet desire to engage in high quality close interpersonal relationships.
    d. the desire to not have too many people around oneself regardless of circumstances.

2. The sexual revolution involved all of the following, *except*
    a. fear of sexual disease.
    b. acceptance of premarital sexual intercourse.
    c. a greater tolerance of sexual practices in general.
    d. a disappearance of sex differences in sexual experience.

3. Cohabiting of unmarried couples is
    a. a strong predictor of marital discord.
    b. on the decline.
    c. against the law in many states.
    d. unrelated to (eventual) marital satisfaction.

4. Passionate love is characterized by
    a. falling head over heels.
    b. thoughtfulness.
    c. a certain comfortable feeling.
    d. initially very little sexual interest.

5. Married people tend to be
    a. universally unhappy.
    b. fairly unhappy, even though historically they used to be extremely happy.
    c. happy, even though they used to be fairly unhappy until recently.
    d. happier than those who aren't married.

6. Women tend to have ____ close friendships compared to men.
    a. ambivalent
    b. superficial
    c. fewer
    d. more

7. Suppose Ken, a toddler, is separated from his mother for about a half hour. When they are reunited, he rejects his mother and shows emotional restraint towards her. Consistent with initial conceptualization of attachment, Ken would have a(n) ____ attachment.
    a. secure
    b. generic insecure
    c. avoidant
    d. ambivalent

8. Jordan has a very favorable view of himself, yet most others don't describe him in favorable terms. As such, he'd likely be classified as having a ____ attachment style.
    a. fearful-avoidant
    b. dismissing
    c. secure
    d. preoccupied

9. Sally is receiving intervention and treatment for her feelings of loneliness, whereby a therapist encourages her to think differently about herself and her life. This type of intervention is chiefly known as
    a. client-centered therapy.
    b. desensitization.
    c. social skills training.
    d. cognitive therapy.

10. Of the following, ____ is considered to be one of the Hendrick's love styles.
    a. agog
    b. thanatos
    c. pragma
    d. alpha

161

2. **Loneliness**
Provide a brief overview of the two primary interventions that are often used for individuals to combat their feelings of loneliness.

3. **Love**
Bret constantly thinks of his new girlfriend, Holly. He often feels that he has an overwhelming, all-consuming love for her. As such, what type of love does this illustrate?

4. **Sexuality**
Contrast the characteristics of an unrestricted sociosexual orientation with a restricted sociosexual orientation.

5. **Marriage**
Discuss the importance of love in a marriage. In particular, what type of love appears to be *most* important in a happy marriage?

9 SOCIAL INFLUENCE: CHANGING OTHERS' BEHAVIOR

Before you read . . .

This chapter discusses various forms of social influence or how individuals try to get us to change our attitudes or behaviors. In this chapter, you'll read about two of social psychology's all-time classic studies. First, you'll consider Solomon Asch's famous conformity studies. You might be surprised at how seemingly easy it is for us to "go along" with others. Even though there are many reasons why we might just go along with others, you'll also consider why sometime we don't (or can't) do that. A consideration of how minorities can influence the majority is also presented. Then, the chapter shifts its focus to the study of compliance and how we respond to others' direct requests. Did you know that many individuals, such as salespersons and politicians, craft their careers around how to successfully use various compliance techniques? In this chapter, you'll be reviewing these major tactics. You'll conclude this chapter by considering extreme forms of social influence. First, you'll consider the nature of obedience by focusing on the second of this chapter's extremely prominent studies—Stanley Milgram's studies of obedience. Afterward, you will consider another (even more) extreme form of social influence, intense indoctrination; this type of social influence helps to explain why cults and other extremist groups are often so successful at getting and keeping members.

Chapter Objectives

After reading this chapter, you should be able to:

- Explain the differences among conformity, compliance, obedience, and intense indoctrination.

- Explain what a "social norm" is and how it functions.

- Outline the methods, goals, and general findings from Asch's famous studies of conformity.

- Consider how cohesiveness and group size affect conformity.

- Contrast descriptive and injunctive norms and, in doing so, state the relevance of normative focus theory.

- Describe how social psychologists have previously and currently study how social norms persist.

- Identify the differences between normative and informational social influence.

165

- Discuss the various reasons why we sometimes do not or cannot conform.

- Consider when and how the minority can influence the majority.

- List the six basic principles of compliance and the seven tactics for gaining compliance that are grounded in these principles. Also, identify two other compliance tactics that are not necessarily rooted in these principles.

- Provide a detailed overview of the initial Milgram obedience study, including its methods, results, and ethical concerns. Also, provide a few examples of subsequent obedience studies conducted by Milgram and these results.

- Describe the social psychological basis for destructive obedience and how individuals can resist its effects.

- Outline the four stages of intense indoctrination and why this form of social influence succeeds.

As you read . . .

Remember this! Below are a list of some of the key terms and concepts from this chapter. Make flashcards in order to enhance your recall ability of these terms. Refer to the definitions that are either in boldface or in the margins of this chapter for help. Be advised that you may also want to include additional terms from this chapter as you deem necessary.

Social influences	Conformity	Compliance
Obedience	Intense indoctrination and its stages	Social norms
Public conformity vs. private acceptance	Cohesiveness	Descriptive vs. injunctive norms
Normative focus theory	Autokinetic phenomenon	Cultures of honor
Normative vs. informational social influence	Jeer pressure	Individuation
Minority influence	Asymmetry model	The six basic principles of compliance
Ingratiation/flattery	Foot-in-the-door technique	Lowball technique
Door-in-the-face technique	"That's-not-all" technique	Playing hard to get
Deadline technique	Pique technique	The velvet glove
The design and ethics of Milgram's study	The design of Asch's study	Destructive obedience
Disobedient models	Reduced attentional capacity	

Conformity: Group Influence in Action

➤ Asch's Research on Conformity: Social Pressure—the Irresistible Force

1. **Match it!** Match each phrase, word, or sentence on the left side of the page with an identifying concept on the right side of the page. Note that each item on the right should be used *only once*.

   ___1. Used primarily by extremist groups   A. conformity

   ___2. Ordering people to do certain behaviors   B. obedience

   ___3. Behaving in ways that are appropriate in a group or society   C. compliance

   ___4. Efforts to get others to say "yes" to a request   D. intense indoctrination

2. Listed below are a variety of social norms. Underline those that are explicit and circle those that are implicit.

   "Don't stand too close to strangers"   "No radio playing on the bus!"

   "Keep off the grass"   "Arrive at parties fashionably late"

   "No littering--$50 fine"   "Tip your waitperson"

3. *"There's a whole lot of numbers going on...!"* In Asch's famous line-judgment task study, there were, in fact, many numbers of relevance. For each number listed below, explain its relevance in terms of the Asch study.

   a.) Usually six to eight:

   b.) 76 percent:

   c.) 37 percent:

   d.) 5 percent:

   e.) 25 percent:

167

4. What's the difference between "public conformity" and "private acceptance?"

➤ Factors Affecting Conformity: Variables That Determine the Extent to Which We "Go Along"

1. Match it! Match each phrase, word, or sentence on the left side of the page with an identifying concept on the right side of the page. Note that each item on the right should be used *only once*.

    ___1. What most people do in a given situation   A. increases conformity

    ___2. The degree of attraction felt by an individual toward an   B. normative focus theory
          influencing group

    ___3. What ought to be done   C. descriptive norms

    ___4. Increasing the group size   D. cohesiveness

    ___5. Norms influence behavior if they're relevant for the person   E. injunctive norms

➤ Social Psychology: Thirty Years of Progress...The Persistence of Social Norms: From the Autokinetic Phenomenon to the "Culture of Honor"

1. Compare and contrast how social psychologists studied the persistence of social norms in the 1930s as opposed to thirty years ago, (Then) versus the more current views on this topic (Now).
        <u>Then</u>   <u>Now</u>

> ## The Bases of Conformity: Why We Often Choose to "Go Along"

1. Contrast normative social influence with informational social influence in terms of their impact on why we often conform.

2. What are the effects of conformity on those who feel that their own judgment is correct, but at the same time, they don't want to be different?

> ## Resisting Pressures to Conform: Why, Sometimes, We Choose *Not* to Go Along

1. Complete the chart below by noting why the following factors may *not* allow or cause a person to NOT conform.

Factor	Why conformity doesn't happen
A desire for individuation	
A desire to retain control	
Having a physical disability	
Being homosexual	

➤ <u>**Minority Influence: Does the Majority Always Rule?**</u>

1. When precisely do minorities succeed in influencing majorities?

2. What happens to minorities when they become the favored position?

3. Even if the minority view doesn't prevail, minorities often produce a positive effect nonetheless. What is this effect?

Compliance: To Ask—Sometimes—Is to Receive

➤ Compliance: The Underlying Principle

1. Evaluate each of the following hypothetical statements and then decide which principle of compliance it represents:

a.) "I bought that vase because they don't make vases like that anymore!" _____

b.) "I'll do that favor for you, Tony, because you're a good guy." _____

c.) "Sure, Pat, you helped me when I was down and out, so helping you is the least I can do."

_____

d.) "After hearing Professor Smith's lecture on the benefits of exercise, I've decided to start my own

exercise program." _____

e.) "I told her that I'd have that report for her by Friday, so I must do it." _____

f.) "Everyone I know seems to be trying this new sandwich, so I'll give it a try." _____

➤ Tactics Based on Friendship or Liking: Ingratiation

1. What is the purpose of ingratiation? What's generally considered to be the best form of ingratiation?

➤ Tactics Based on Commitment or Consistency: The Foot-in-the-Door and the Lowball

1. Compare and contrast the foot-in-the-door technique with the lowball technique by explaining how each operates.

➢ **Tactics Based on Reciprocity: The Door-in-the-Face and the "That's-Not-All Techniques**

1. Compare and contrast the door-in-the-face technique with the "that's-not-all" technique by explaining how each operates.

➢ **Tactics Based on Scarcity: Playing Hard to Get and the Fast-Approaching-Deadline Technique**

1. Compare and contrast the playing hard to get technique with the deadline technique by explaining how each operates.

➢ **Other Tactics for Gaining Compliance: The Pique Technique and Putting Others in a Good Mood**

1. Explain how and why the pique technique and being in a good mood can increase compliance.

➤ **Beyond The Headlines: As Social Psychologists See It...High-Pressure Tactics for Gaining Compliance: Do You Really Need a $1,500 Vacuum Cleaner? Does Anyone?**

1. Discuss how Kirby salesmen are able to sell such pricey vacuums to people (particularly the elderly) who really don't need such vacuums. Do you think anything can be done to ensure that unsuspecting people won't (effectively) be coaxed to buy something they really can't afford?

Extreme Forms of Social Influence: Obedience to Authority and Intense Indoctrination

---

➤ **Destructive Obedience: Would You Harm an Innocent Stranger If Ordered to Do So?**

1. Persons who possess authority and could use it tend to prefer to exert influence through the "velvet glove" meaning that _____.

2. Stanley Milgram's interest in studying destructive obedience came apart, in part, from a desire to understand the horrors of _____.

3. Outline, step by step, what each of Milgram's subjects (teachers") did as they participated in Milgram's initial study of obedience.

4. _____ percent of Milgram's participants showed total obedience in his initial obedience study.

5. Identify two variations of the Milgram obedience study and summarize the results from these follow-up studies.

6. What were the ethical concerns associated with Milgram's study? Could Milgram's study be done today in the U.S.? Why?

7. Why does destructive obedience occur in natural settings?

8. Identify four ways to resist the effects of destructive obedience.

➢ Intense Indoctrination: Social Influence Carried to the Extreme

1. Identify and describe the four stages of intense indoctrination.

2. What is the primary reason why intense indoctrination often succeeds?

Thinking about The Aftermath of the September 11, 2001 Attacks and Social Influence

Make the case that followers of Osama bin Laden and the al-Qaeda terrorist groups are brought into this organization through destructive obedience and intense indoctrination.

After you read . . . Practice Tests

Practice Test 1

1. ____ is an effort to get others to say yes to various requests, whereas ____ is behaving in ways that are appropriate in our group or society.
   a. Conformity; compliance
   b. Compliance; conformity
   c. Obedience; compliance
   d. Obedience; conformity

2. ____ norms govern how individuals are expected to behave in specific situations.
   a. Societal
   b. Social
   c. Personal
   d. Explicit

3. In Asch's famous conformity studies, roughly ____ percent of his subjects never yielded to the group pressure.
   a. 5
   b. 15
   c. 25
   d. 75

4. When cohesiveness is ____, people tend to conform.
   a. absent
   b. low
   c. moderate
   d. high

5. Suppose that Irene, after noticing a large road sign stating, "No littering—$500 fine," followed by spotting a nearby police car, decides that it isn't wise to throw her empty soda can from her car window as she had planned. Her actions can be *best* understood according to ____.
   a. injunctive norm salience
   b. normative focus theory
   c. descriptive norms
   d. explicit social norms

6. In which of the following American cities (or geographical regions) would it be *least* likely to observe cultures of honor?
   a. Denver, Colorado
   b. Pittsburgh, Pennsylvania
   c. Savannah, Georgia
   d. Cheyenne, Wyoming

7. Concerns about jeer pressure are closely linked with the importance of
    a. normative social influence.
    b. informational social influence.
    c. individuation.
    d. minority influence.

8. The need for individuation ____ across cultures such that individuation ____.
    a. is constant; is equally likely to occur in collectivistic and individualistic societies.
    b. varies greatly; occurs more regularly in collectivistic than individualistic societies.
    c. varies greatly; occurs more regularly in individualistic than collectivistic societies.
    d. is rarely found; is typically viewed as antagonistic against one's group (regardless of culture).

9. All of the following factors increase the possibility that a minority will alter the majority view, *except*
    a. consistency.
    b. flexibility.
    c. operating within the current social context.
    d. angrily expressing views.

10. A minority that has managed to become the majority is often considered to be ____ during their early stages as a group.
    a. vulnerable
    b. unrealistic
    c. overly positive
    d. dogmatic

Practice Test 2

1. All of the following careers are often synonymous with "compliance professionals," *except*
    a. advertisers.
    b. politicians.
    c. salespeople.
    d. medical doctors.

2. The notion that we try to secure outcomes or objects that are decreasing in their availability is known as
    a. social validation.
    b. commitment.
    c. scarcity.
    d. reciprocity.

3. Ingratiation is considered to be a compliance tactic based on
    a. scarcity.
    b. commitment.
    c. authority.
    d. liking.

4. Sarah, a teenager, knows that her mother won't allow her to stay out past midnight with her friends on a Saturday night, but is hoping to stay out until midnight. So, when Sarah asks her mom if she can stay out until 2 a.m. When her mom refuses, Sarah then asks "Well then, can I at least stay out until midnight?" Reluctantly, her mom agrees with Sarah's request. This example illustrates the
   a. foot-in-the-door technique.
   b. door-in-the-face technique.
   c. lowball technique.
   d. deadline technique.

5. If you've agreed to purchase something after a salesperson has decided to sweeten the deal, you've likely shown compliance as a result of the
   a. lowball technique.
   b. "that's-not-all" technique.
   c. pique technique.
   d. playing hard to get technique.

6. When individuals use the _____ technique in the area of romance by suggesting that it is difficult to win their affections, this tends to _____ their desirability.
   a. playing hard to get; increases
   b. playing hard to get; decreases
   c. pique technique; increases
   d. pique technique; decreases

7. Suppose Iris decides to buy a certain shirt because she claims "it's what everyone who's like me is wearing." This example depicts the importance of compliance tactics based on
   a. scarcity.
   b. liking.
   c. authority.
   d. social validation.

8. The pique technique often gains compliance due to the fact that
   a. we feel that when something is rare, it has inherent value.
   b. we're more likely to say "yes" to a request when we're in a good mood.
   c. unusual requests often stimulate our interest.
   d. when we are threatened, we often feel that we have no choice but to comply.

9. Rind and Bordia (1996) found that when female and male waitpersons drew a smiley face on the back of a check for customers,
   a. this did not affect either of their tips.
   b. this increased the females' and males' tips.
   c. this increased the females' and decreased the males' tips.
   d. this increased the females' tips but did not affect the males' tips.

10. Your text authors report that Kirby salespersons are quite effective at selling expensive vacuum cleaners by using all of the following techniques, *except*
    a. the door-in-the-face.
    b. the foot-in-the-door.
    c. the deadline technique.
    d. the pique technique.

Practice Test 3

1. Those who possess authority tend to prefer to use it by making
    a. direct orders.
    b. requests.
    c. explicit threats.
    d. subtle hints.

2. Milgram began his interest in obedience with an attempt to better understand the events surrounding
    a. the Civil War.
    b. World War I.
    c. the Great Depression.
    d. the Holocaust.

3. In Milgram's obedience studies, the research participant was referred to as the
    a. experimenter.
    b. teacher.
    c. learner.
    d. victim.

4. In Milgram's initial obedience study, electric shocks were used
    a. every time the learner gave an incorrect response.
    b. any time the teacher felt like giving one.
    c. at no time whatsoever.
    d. only once on the research participant in order to convince him that the shocks were "real."

5. In the initial obedience study, Milgram found that ____ percent of his subjects showed total obedience.
    a. 25
    b. 45
    c. 65
    d. 85

6. A practical consequence of the Milgram study is that it led to
    a. a worldwide understanding of the harmful effects of destructive obedience.
    b. a thorough condemnation of Milgram's work by the psychological community.
    c. stricter ethical guidelines in research.
    d. strong criticism from Holocaust survivors.

7. All of the following are helpful strategies to combat destructive obedience, *except*
   a. reminding individuals that they, not the authorities, are responsible for harm that they cause.
   b. highlighting disobedient models.
   c. accepting the motives and expertise of authority figures for what they are.
   d. being aware of the power of authority to command blind obedience.

8. A successful example of where the power of authority was resisted in order to produce positive outcomes was
   a. the overthrow of many Eastern European governments in the 1980s and 1990s.
   b. when Linda Tripp revealed her incriminating conversations with Monica Lewinsky.
   c. the oil embargo of the 1970s.
   d. when the U.S. Supreme Court ruled in George W. Bush's favor in the *Bush v. Gore* case.

9. Suppose the al-Qaeda terrorist group is trying to recruit new members. If one of the recruits is asked to pay lip service to the demands and beliefs of the group and to actively "try out" the role of member, then he is in the _____ stage of intense indoctrination.
   a. compliance
   b. consolidation
   c. softening-up
   d. internalization

10. The key reason why intense indoctrination often succeeds is due to
    a. increased attentional capacity.
    b. decreased attentional capacity.
    c. heightened awareness of one's mortality.
    d. heightened awareness of other's mortality.

Comprehensive Test
(NOTE: Items 1-15 are multiple-choice questions and items 16-23 are true-false questions.)

1. "Private acceptance" refers to
   a. going along with others to save yourself embarrassment.
   b. going along within oneself, but openly defying the group.
   c. actually coming to think and feel as the group does.
   d. actually declaring publicly that you believe as the group does.

2. An example of an unwritten norm would be:
   a. "Posted speed is 65. No tolerance!"
   b. "Those above the age of seventy are granted a lower tax rate by order of the city council."
   c. "One should not break into a line of people waiting."
   d. "Students not registered by August 28 will be charged a late fee."

3. Widespread disobeying of social norms would lead to
    a. social chaos.
    b. teaching children not to be slavish conformists.
    c. lowering the authoritarianism of the population.
    d. more questioning of the government than other institutions.

4. In Milgram's original obedience study,
    a. the experimenter pressured subjects to continue the experiment, even when the "victim" signified distress.
    b. the subjects were told that they were responsible for the "victim's" welfare.
    c. strong shocks were actually delivered to the "victim."
    d. there was a much higher rate of obedience than when Milgram moved his study from Yale to a rundown office building.

5. Social influence is
    a. simply being influenced by others.
    b. the influence of society on us.
    c. influencing how society operates in the present and future.
    d. the efforts on the part of an individual to alter the behavior or attitudes of others.

6. Conformity occurs when individuals
    a. change their behavior in order to fit that of other persons in their group.
    b. question the conventions of a society.
    c. mimic each other.
    d. respond favorably to a person's direct request.

7. Overall, _____ percent of Asch's participants voiced agreement with the collaborators' false judgments.
    a. 37
    b. 76
    c. 5
    d. 65

8. Milgram reduced the overall level of obedience to thirty percent when
    a. the learner complained of pain.
    b. he conducted the experiment away from the prestigious Yale University.
    c. the subject heard pounding on a wall by the learner.
    d. the subject had to actually place the learner's hand on a shock plate.

9. The power of authority in Milgram's experiments was in large part to due to his
    a. threats of punishment to the subject if he didn't obey.
    b. availability of great personal rewards for those subjects who did obey.
    c. release of participants from responsibility.
    d. ability to recruit particularly sadistic individuals for his studies.

10. Efforts by extremist groups to recruit new members and induce them to accept the group's beliefs is known as
    a. obedience.
    b. conformity.
    c. compliance.
    d. intense indoctrination.

11. A common theme shared between research involving the autokinetic phenomenon and cultures of honor is that
    a. people tend to be overly gullible and rarely use their intelligence when in a group.
    b. once norms are created, they tend to persist.
    c. the Southern and Western parts of the United States tend to feature a culture in which it is acceptable to use violence in order to defend one's honor.
    d. even though norms can be informative, these often cause individuals to lose sight of what is morally correct.

12. Suppose a minority fails to influence the majority on some issue. A possible consequence of this action is that
    a. it will serve as an impetus for the minority to become radical.
    b. it will serve as an impetus for the majority to become radical.
    c. it may cause the majority to engage in systematic processing.
    d. the minority view will likely be forgotten.

13. A compliance tactic based on reciprocity is the
    a. lowball technique.
    b. foot-in-the-door technique.
    c. door-in-the-face technique.
    d. playing hard to get technique.

14. Suppose one of Jill's classmates ask her if he can borrow her watch for fifty minutes so that he can pace himself during his history exam. Taken by the unusual nature of his request, she agrees to allow her classmate to use her watch. This example highlights the
    a. "that's-not-all" technique.
    b. pique technique.
    c. foot-in-the-door technique.
    d. lowball technique.

15. The third stage of intense indoctrination is
    a. softening-up.
    b. internalization.
    c. consolidation.
    d. compliance.

16. The desire to be liked and correct are two powerful reasons why we conform.

17. In Asch's famous conformity studies, about a quarter of subjects went along with the false judgment at least once.

18. Public conformity tends to routinely predict private acceptance.

19. The principle of reciprocity provides the basis for the "that's-not-all" technique.

20. Jack, a waiter at a trendy restaurant, places smiley faces on a customer's bill. In doing so, he should see an increase in his tips.

21. If you comply with an unusual request, then you have likely been influenced by the pique technique.

22. Gradual escalation of shock levels in the Milgram study served to lower obedience.

23. Special uniforms, badges, and titles do little to increase the power of authority.

When You Have Finished . . .

TOP TEN REASONS WHY SOCIAL INFLUENCE HAS GREAT RELEVANCE FOR *YOUR* LIFE

1. We frequently experience direct or indirect pressure to change our views or behaviors in some way. This is what social influence is all about!

2. By being aware of the various compliance tactics, we are less likely to be hoodwinked into accepting a deal of some sort that really isn't much of a bargain.

3. Despite the fact that authority figures can exert a tremendous amount of pressure for us to obey their commands, we should also be aware that there are ways to combat destructive obedience.

4. If you ever find yourself in a minority role, then you will want to note the most effective ways to influence a majority.

5. By understanding the nature of conformity, you will have a better appreciation for why we often "go along" and why this isn't always a "bad thing."

Let's reflect on point #3 and, more specifically, on Milgram's classic study of obedience. How do YOU think you would've act if you were a research participant in Milgram's initial study of obedience? If you say that you would *not* go along with the experimenter's orders, how can you be so sure that you wouldn't simply obey?

Short Answer/Essay Questions

1. **Social Influence Categories**
   Even though Mary's friends do *not* explicitly tell or ask her to drink some alcohol, she feels a certain amount of pressure to do so. What type of social influence does this illustrate?

2. **The Persistence of Social Norms**
   Describe what is meant by a "culture of honor" and where such cultures are found within the United States.

3. **Minority Influence**
   State the three key factors that need to be in place in order for the minority to have a viable chance to influence the majority.

4. **Compliance Tactics**
   Joe is negotiating with Sal, who is trying to sell his home. Immediately after Sal tells Joe that he'll sell his house for $120,000, he says that "I'll pay for all of your closing costs." What type of compliance tactic does this illustrate?

5. **Milgram's Studies of Obedience**
    Briefly outline two other follow-up studies Milgram conducted after his initial study of obedience. What were the results?

10 PROSOCIAL BEHAVIOR:
HELPING OTHERS

Before you read . . .

This chapter reviews research regarding prosocial or helping behavior. You'll learn very quickly that there are many important factors to consider when trying to determine whether an individual will help someone in an emergency. It truly is amazing how many factors can determine whether one helps—everything from whether others are around to individual difference or personality factors and motivational or emotional states. It's also interesting to note that who you are (or appear to be) can influence whether you receive help; this chapter will consider these factors. You should also be aware that social psychologists have long considered why people decide to help others in the first place. You will be reviewing the major four hypotheses regarding this issue.

Chapter Objectives

After reading this chapter, you should be able to:

- Explain the key differences between "prosocial behavior" and "altruism."

- Analyze how the murder of Kitty Genovese led to a greater understanding of when and why a person may (or may not) choose to help in an emergency.

- Outline Latane and Darley's (1971) five essential steps to a prosocial response in an emergency and note at what point help may be given.

- Discuss three important situational factors that can either enhance or inhibit helping.

- Contrast the following terms: egoism, self-interest, moral integrity, and moral hypocrisy.

- Explain how a bystander's emotional state may influence his or her decision to help.

- Discuss the nature of empathy, how it develops, and why people may differ as a function of it.

- Note the factors that may cause a person to help someone who has been the victim of a catastrophe and why these factors may *not* be relevant to the September 11, 2001 tragedy.

- Outline other personality factors (other than empathy) associated with prosocial behavior and pay particular attention to the qualities of the altruistic personality.

- Explain the various motives for volunteering.

- Consider the role that gender plays in helping behavior.

- Note the general reactions of those who receive help in terms of how it feels to receive such assistance.

- State, define, and contrast the four key models or hypotheses of why we engage in prosocial behavior.

As you read . . .

> Remember this! Below are a list of some of the key terms and concepts from this chapter. Make flashcards in order to enhance your recall ability of these terms. Refer to the definitions that are either in boldface or in the margins of this chapter for help. Be advised that you may also want to include additional terms from this chapter as you deem necessary.

Prosocial behavior	Altruism	Diffusion of responsibility
Bystander effect	Latane and Darley's five step model	Pluralistic ignorance
Prosocial models	Egoism	Self-interest
Moral integrity	Moral hypocrisy	Empathy and its components
The major types of perspective taking	Need for approval	Interpersonal trust
Machiavellianism	Altruistic personality and its components	Volunteering and its functions
Generativity	Empathy-altruism hypothesis	Negative-state relief model
Empathic joy hypothesis	Genetic determinism model	Empathy avoidance
Selective altruism	Helper's high	

Responding to an Emergency: Why Are Bystanders Sometimes Helpful, Sometimes Indifferent?

1. What's the key difference between "prosocial behavior" and "altruism?"

➤ Social Psychology: Thirty Years of Progress...The Study of Prosocial Behavior Began with a Murder

1. Since your authors note that much of the rest of this chapter summarizes the "now" component of prosocial behavior, it isn't quite appropriate for us to make a comparison of "then" and "now" as we've done in the previous chapters. However, let's reflect on the "then" component by discussing how the study of prosocial behavior began—and it was with the murder of Kitty Genovese. Briefly summarize the events of this infamous murder.

2. In your own words, what's the difference between "diffusion of responsibility" and the "bystander effect?" How might these factors account for the Genovese murder?

3. Describe how Darley and Latane (1968) demonstrated the bystander effect in the laboratory.

➤ Why Didn't Someone Help?

1. To what degree do *you* believe that diffusion of responsibility and the bystander effect accounts for why people often don't offer help in an emergency?

➤ **The Decision to Help in an Emergency: Five Essential Steps**

1. Complete the following flowchart that outlines Latane and Darley's five essential steps to a prosocial response in an emergency. (You may want to pay particular attention to the chart on page 394 in your text.)

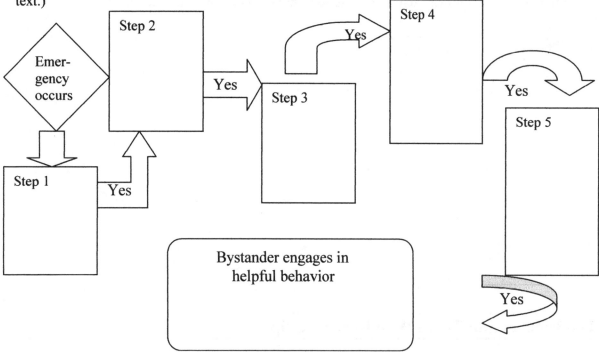

If the answer is "no" to any of these questions then _____

_____.

➤ **Situational Factors That Enhance or Inhibit Helping: Attraction, Attributions, and Prosocial Models**

1. *To help or not to help, that is the question.* For each of the following situations, indicate whether help will be offered.

a.) Helping a stranger who appears similar to you in some way: _____

b.) Helping a stranger with a stigma: _____

c.) Helping someone whose problems are perceived as controllable: _____

d.) Helping someone who appears too much like yourself: _____

e.) Helping someone after watching the TV show, *Lassie*: _____

f.) Helping someone after watching the TV show, *South Park*: _____

➢ <u>Self-Interest, Moral Integrity, and Moral Hypocrisy</u>

1. Differentiate the following terms: egoism, self-interest, moral integrity, and moral hypocrisy.

The Helpers and Those Who Receive Help

➢ <u>Helping as a Function of the Bystander's Emotional State</u>

1. As your text notes, there is a common belief that being in a good mood makes it more likely that you'll help someone, whereas being in a negative mood has the opposite effect. Describe the evidence that *supports* these claims as well as instances that does *not support* these claims.

➢ **Dispositional Differences in Prosocial Responding**

1. What's wrong here? Each of the following statements is *false*. Modify the statement in some way in order to make it correct.

    a.) Empathy simply involves an affective component.

    b.) When someone feels empathy for a fictional character, they're taking the "imagine other" perspective.

    c.) Empathy does *not* have a genetic component whatsoever.

    d.) Robert Coles believes that children can learn empathy by remembering a variety of social rules and regulations.

    e.) Women are just as likely as men to show prosocial behavior.

    f.) People tend to help the victims of a disaster no matter what.

    g.) Just as in the Kitty Genovese case, New Yorkers appeared indifferent to the needs of the victims of the September 11, 2001 disaster unless they were personally affected in some way.

    h.) Those who have a low need for approval and high levels of Machiavellianism are particularly likely to offer help.

2. State and define the five components of the altruistic personality.

> ## Beyond The Headlines: As Social Psychologists See It...Prosocial Responding to an Apparent Crime

1. Briefly discuss why the cab driver helped two strangers, even though an actual crime wasn't committed? Do you think such an incident is an example of an "only in New York" story or could it have happened anywhere?

> ## Volunteering: Motivation for Long-Term Help

1. Identify some of the key reasons why a person might volunteer. In doing so, emphasize the rationale for AIDS volunteerism, as well as the role of generativity in volunteering.

➤ Who Receives Help, and How Do People Respond to Being Helped?

1. Complete the following sentences by underlining the term or phrase that makes the statement correct.

    a.) Men are (likely, unlikely) to help women in distress.

    b.) A possible reason why men may help women in distress may be related to the (third, fourth) step of Darley and Latane's model of helping behavior.

    c.) Men who are driving (alone, with other male friends) are likely to help a female who's experiencing car trouble.

    d.) (Elderly, young) adults don't readily ask for help that often.

    e.) After you receive help, it is fairly common to experience (overwhelming happiness, discomfort).

Explaining Prosocial Behavior: Why Do People Help?

➤ Empathy-Altruism: It Feels Good to Help Those in Need

1. Match it! Match each phrase, word, or sentence on the left side of the page with an identifying concept on the right side of the page. Note that each item on the right should be used *only once*.

    ___1. Helping that has evolutionary benefits   A. empathic joy hypothesis

    ___2. Helping that makes the helper feel good   B. genetic determinism model

    ___3. Empathy directed at a single group member   C. empathy-altruism hypothesis

    ___4. Helping done in order to make the helper have   D. empathy avoidance
          less negative affect

    ___5. Helping simply done for the sake of helping   E. selective altruism

    ___6. A motivation to not engage in high-cost helping   F. negative-state relief model

---

➤ Negative-State Relief: Helping Can Reduce Your Negative Affect

1. Consistent with the negative-state relief model, it doesn't matter whether the bystander's negative

    emotions were _____

    _____.

➤ Empathic Joy: Helping Can Make You Feel Better—If You Know That You Accomplished Something

1. The emotion that is elicited by performing a prosocial act is sometimes called _____,

   which refers to _____.

➤ Genetic Determinism: Helping Others Maximizes Gene Survival

1. Consistent with the genetic determinism model, we tend to help our _____, particularly

   those who are _____.

Thinking about The Aftermath of the September 11, 2001 Attacks and Prosocial Behavior

Your text makes the very valid point that those who help others often risk their own lives in doing so. Tragically, that was the case on September eleventh, when hundreds of heroic firefighters, police officers, and other emergency service personnel died while trying to save and rescue others. Do you believe that these individuals truly knew the danger that they were facing as they climbed the Twin Towers? In hindsight, do you think that these individuals should have been sent up to rescue others as they did that tragic day?

After you read . . . Practice Tests

Practice Test 1

1. _____ is an unselfish concern for the welfare of others.
   a. Empathy
   b. Sympathy
   c. Altruism
   d. Prosocial behavior

2. An important lesson from the infamous Kitty Genovese murder is that people tend to
   a. feel indifferent about crime and crime victims.
   b. be apathetic, unless a matter directly concerns them.
   c. people are much less likely to help when others are around.
   d. offer help to others, only if they live in a rural area.

3. A key reason why the bystander effect occurs is that people tend to
   a. gawk and stare when an accident or emergency occurs.
   b. only focus on their own well-being during an emergency.
   c. feel less responsible for offering aid to a victim.
   d. denigrate the victim and wonder whether he or she caused their lot.

4. According to Latane and Darley (1970), there are _____ essential steps to responding to an emergency.
   a. three
   b. four
   c. five
   d. six

5. A bystander will offer help, according to Latane and Darley's (1970) model if an affirmative response is given to _____ of the stages.
   a. all
   b. a majority
   c. none
   d. any

6. Interpreting an emergency as such is considered the _____ stage of the Latane and Darley (1970) model.
   a. first
   b. second
   c. third
   d. fourth

7. Of the following, an individual would be *most* likely to help a stranger who
   a. appeared to be involved in some domestic dispute.
   b. had a stigma of some sort.
   c. appears to be similar to the individual in some way.
   d. appears to have caused his or her dilemma in some way.

8. Non-prosocial models that aren't necessarily violent, such as the characters on *South Park*, appear to
   a. surprisingly enhance prosocial behavior in others.
   b. adversely affect prosocial behavior in others.
   c. have no effect whatsoever on prosocial behavior.
   d. impact individuals in ways that have not yet been fully examined by researchers.

9. ____ is an exclusive concern with one's own personal needs.
   a. Egoism
   b. Self-interest
   c. Moral integrity
   d. Moral hypocrisy

10. When faced with a certain moral dilemma, Marilyn decides to perform a behavior that satisfies her own needs and desires. In this example, it appears that Marilyn's ____ was stronger than her ____.
   a. moral hypocrisy; moral integrity
   b. self-interest; moral integrity
   c. moral integrity; moral hypocrisy
   d. self-interest; moral hypocrisy

Practice Test 2

1. If a person is in a good mood and is faced with a situation that might require him or her to help,
   a. assistance is uniformly given.
   b. he or she will likely do so provided that his or her prosocial act doesn't spoil his or her good mood.
   c. such an individual tends to shy away from offering help.
   d. he or she will only offer help if his or her positive mood is due to situational causes.

2. Empathy has a(n)
   a. affective component only.
   b. cognitive component only.
   c. affective and a cognitive component.
   d. biological component only.

3. The Native American expression, "walking a mile in my moccasins," pertains to the ____ aspect of empathy.
   a. feeling sympathetic
   b. perspective taking
   c. altruistic
   d. personality

4. Apparently, genetics is ____ involved in affective empathy and is ____ involved in cognitive empathy.
   a. partially; partially
   b. not; not
   c. not; partially
   d. partially; not

5. Some psychologists suggest that the key to fostering prosocial behavior in children is to
   a. keep them away from television.
   b. teach them to be kind.
   c. instruct them about the benefits of helping.
   d. simply attend church on a regular basis.

6. During the Nazi Holocaust, the gender breakdown of non-Jewish Germans who helped rescue Jews tended to be
   a. women by a ratio of two to one.
   b. men by a ratio of two to one.
   c. women by a ratio of four to one.
   d. an equal ratio of men and women.

7. Suppose Bill, a conservative, and Tom, a liberal, learn that a major flood has hit a town bordering the Ohio River in the United States. Who is *most* likely to help?
   a. Bill
   b. Tom
   c. They are equally likely to help.
   d. Since political ideology doesn't predict helping in the wake of a disaster, more information is needed in order to answer this question.

8. Among the many lessons of the September 11, 2001 catastrophe is that
   a. people tend to help as a means of expressing relief that they haven't been personally affected by a disaster.
   b. in order for a people to help in a major catastrophe, they must feel some sort of similarity to the victims.
   c. people usually don't offer help to victims unless they have personally experienced such a disaster.
   d. a helper often jeopardizes his or her life when offering assistance.

9. Empathy tends to be ____ related to achievement motivation and ____ related to aggression.
   a. positively; negatively
   b. negatively; not
   c. not; negatively
   d. not; not

10. All of the following are components of the altruistic personality, *except*
   a. the belief in a just world.
   b. low egocentrism.
   c. an external locus of control.
   d. social responsibility.

Practice Test 3

1. AIDS volunteerism
   a. has greatly increased in recent years since most people don't fear AIDS anymore.
   b. is just as likely to occur for a homosexual or drug user than for someone who got AIDS through a blood transfusion.
   c. is often viewed by potential volunteers as having too many costs associated with it.
   d. usually is not viewed as personally rewarding by those who partake in it.

2. The protective function of volunteerism allows a person to
   a. potentially address personal problems.
   b. act on important values.
   c. grow and develop psychologically.
   d. gain career-related experience.

3. ____ are particularly likely to help a female motorist with car trouble.
   a. Young men driving alone
   b. Young men driving with other men
   c. Middle-aged men
   d. Women

4. A fairly common reaction from individuals who receive help is
   a. relief.
   b. profound gratitude.
   c. feeling overjoyed.
   d. discomfort.

5. Of the following groups, ____ are the *most* likely to ask for help.
   a. elderly adults
   b. those with an ambivalent attachment style
   c. those with low socioeconomic status
   d. young adults

6. The _____ states that prosocial behavior is motivated solely by the desire to help someone in need.
   a. genetic determinism model
   b. empathy-altruism hypothesis
   c. empathic joy hypothesis
   d. negative-state relief model

7. Even though Jean was interested in working at a battered women's shelter, once she realized that the cost of helping was high, her interest in helping dramatically decreased. This example illustrates
   a. empathy avoidance.
   b. selective altruism.
   c. empathic joy.
   d. a helper's high.

8. Since Jon was in a foul mood, he decided to offer assistance to a man who just fell in the hope of making himself feel better. The _____ is probably provides the *best* explanation for why Jon offered help.
   a. genetic determinism model
   b. empathy-altruism hypothesis
   c. empathic joy hypothesis
   d. negative-state relief model

9. Of the four major explanations for prosocial behavior, the one that does *not* emphasize the role of emotion is the
   a. genetic determinism model.
   b. empathy-altruism hypothesis.
   c. empathic joy hypothesis.
   d. negative-state relief model.

10. There is some empirical evidence that shows that you are *most* likely to help
    a. any person with whom you have a close relationship.
    b. a fairly close relative regardless of their age or gender.
    c. a fairly young, close relative.
    d. any biological relative.

Comprehensive Test
(NOTE: Items 1-15 are multiple-choice questions and items 16-23 are true-false questions.)

1. The bystander effect refers to the
   a. inhibition of helping when there are several witnesses present during an emergency.
   b. indifference to the plight of someone in distress.
   c. apathy shown by the victim of a calamity.
   d. tendency for people to "kick someone when he or she is down."

2. Diffusion of responsibility involves
   a. spreading the responsibility for helping from oneself to others present in an emergency.
   b. absorbing the responsibility to help from others present in an emergency.
   c. whether and why someone helps when there is only a single witness to an emergency.
   d. the techniques needed in order to help someone in a responsible and thoughtful manner.

3. According to Robert Coles, children learn moral intelligence
   a. by watching and listening to their parents.
   b. from television.
   c. from their peers.
   d. by learning a set of rules and regulations.

4. Of the following, a(n) _____ is *most* likely to help.
   a. middle-aged person
   b. person with an internal locus of control
   c. individual with a history of having their need for approval punished after helping
   d. male

5. The negative state relief model postulates that
   a. people help in order to reduce a victim's negative affect.
   b. emergency situations cause negative moods.
   c. individuals help in order to relieve his or her own negative emotions.
   d. victims in negative moods are helped less often than those in positive moods.

6. Of the following, the *most* important factor in helping behavior is
   a. a history of being in need of help.
   b. the ability to take the perspective of another person.
   c. one's physical fitness.
   d. having some kind of disability or other affliction.

7. _____ is part of a "helper's high."
   a. Warmth
   b. Relaxation
   c. Contemplation
   d. A peak experience

8. _____ is involved in the empathic joy hypothesis.
   a. Warmth
   b. A peak experience
   c. Feeling good about accomplishing something
   d. Getting rid of a bad mood and putting someone else in a good mood

9. Suppose you are at a movie theater and notice smoke coming from one of the vents in the theater. Even though you and many other people in the audience notice the smoke, no one decides to do anything about it. This illustrates
    a. the bystander effect.
    b. the diffusion of responsibility.
    c. pluralistic ignorance.
    d. moral hypocrisy.

10. Even though Caleb stresses the importance of exercise to others, he rarely exercises himself. This is an example of
    a. moral integrity.
    b. self-interest.
    c. egoism.
    d. moral hypocrisy.

11. The positive effect of negative emotions in helping behavior is *most* likely to be observed if the
    a. negative feelings are very intense.
    b. emergency is not ambiguous.
    c. act of helping will be difficult.
    d. individual usually experiences negative emotions.

12. After watching a very sad movie, Julia feels very sorry for the lead character when he died. Julia's perspective involved
    a. imagining the self.
    b. imagining the other.
    c. fantasy.
    d. theoretical understanding.

13. All of the following personality characteristics contribute to helping behavior, *except*
    a. the need for approval.
    b. sociability.
    c. interpersonal trust.
    d. Machiavellianism.

14. A possible reason why men readily help women may be related to the nature of the ____ stage of Latane and Darley's (1970) model of responding to an emergency.
    a. second
    b. third
    c. fourth
    b. fifth

15. Receiving help often ____ the recipient's self-esteem, particularly if the helper is a ____.
    a. reverses the current state of; stranger
    b. decreases; stranger
    c. increases; friend
    d. decreases; friend

16. Deciding to help is the third step in the sequence leading to helping in an emergency.

17. Being in a positive mood intrinsically increases prosocial behavior.

18. Leon has just retired and is very concerned about the well-being of future generations. As such, his concerns are related to the concept of generativity.

19. Those with an altruistic personality were particularly likely to rescue and help Jews from Nazi persecution.

20. The empathic-joy hypothesis states that individuals are motivated to help in order to reduce one's negative emotional state.

21. Men tend to help because they are more empathic than women.

22. The outpouring of help following the September 11, 2001 disaster revealed that perceived similarity to the victims is a key determinant of prosocial behavior following a catastrophe.

23. There is a definite gene for prosocial behavior.

When You Have Finished . . .

TOP TEN REASONS WHY PROSOCIAL BEHAVIOR HAS GREAT RELEVANCE FOR *YOUR* LIFE

1. Most of us would like to think that if we needed help, it would be offered to us *and* if we could, we'd offer help to others. The study of prosocial behavior helps to pinpoint the conditions when this is most likely to occur.

2. By understanding the five essential steps to helping in an emergency, governmental agencies and laypersons alike can understand why and how individuals may help under these conditions.

3. Parents can certainly benefit from an understanding of the importance of how to foster empathy in their children.

4. Even though it may not represent altruism in the "purest" sense, people may be more likely to help others if they realize that they're more likely to feel good after helping someone.

5. In the aftermath of the September 11, 2001 disaster, we all dramatically witnessed how prosocial behavior from helpers can truly save lives—even though it may potentially take the life of the helper.

Let's try to reflect a bit more on point #4 by thinking about a time when you offered help to someone. Did you truly feel better after doing so? If yes, how? Also, do you think that people can truly show altruism without really expecting *anything* in return? Justify your answer. You may also want to ask this question to your friends and see what they have to say.

Short Answer/Essay Questions

1. **Prosocial Responses in an Emergency**
   Outline Latane and Darley's (1971) model of the five essential steps to a prosocial response in an emergency.

2. **Prosocial Models**
   Briefly describe the three types of models shown on television and other media that may influence a child's prosocial behavior (for better or worse).

3. **Moods and Helping Behavior**
   Briefly discuss when a person who is in a good mood may *not* be likely to help a stranger.

4. **Volunteering**
   Explain why someone might volunteer as a function of generativity.

5. **Theoretical Explanations for Prosocial Behavior**
    Consistent with the genetic determinism model, what type of individual should you be *most* likely to
    help?

11

AGGRESSION:
ITS NATURE, CAUSES, AND CONTROL

Before you read . . .

In many respects, this chapter reflects the exact opposite of the previous chapter on helping behavior—here we look at behavior that is designed to harm others in some way, or aggressive behavior. First, you will consider various theoretical perspectives on aggression: In other words, why should we show aggression anyway? Afterward, you will be presented with a variety of personality/individual difference and social/situational factors that can cause or produce aggression. Then you will consider a couple of examples of aggression that may occur in a long-term relationship—namely, bullying and workplace violence. Finally, you'll consider a variety of practical techniques that may reduce various forms of aggression. You actually might be quite surprised by some of the techniques that can help to reduce aggression—and by some of the popular techniques that do *not* appear to reduce aggression.

Chapter Objectives

After reading this chapter, you should be able to:

- Contrast the views of Freud, Lorenz, and evolutionary perspectives in terms of how aggression develops.

- State the purpose of drive theories of aggression and note the most well-known of these theories.

- Outline the variables involved in the general affective aggression model and briefly explain how this model operates.

- Identify the ways by which social psychologists study aggression in the laboratory.

- Discuss why the original frustration-aggression hypothesis is *not* considered to be accurate by most contemporary social psychologists.

- Outline the major points of excitation transfer theory.

- Identify individual difference or personal causes of aggression by discussing (among others) the Type A behavior pattern, hostile and instrumental aggression, and the hostile attributional bias.

- Identify the nature of gender differences in aggression.

- Discuss how temperature and alcohol may influence aggression.

- Contrast the characteristics of bullies, victims, and bully/victims and note the ways by which bullying behavior can be reduced.

- Note the prevalence of workplace violence and summarize the three main categories of aggression in the workplace.

- Consider whether punishment can be an effective deterrent to violence.

- Evaluate the veracity of the catharsis hypothesis.

- Identify the various techniques (cognitive and non-cognitive interventions) that can be used in order to reduce aggression.

As you read . . .

> **Remember this! Below are a list of some of the key terms and concepts from this chapter. Make flashcards in order to enhance your recall ability of these terms. Refer to the definitions that are either in boldface or in the margins of this chapter for help. Be advised that you may also want to include additional terms from this chapter as you deem necessary.**

Aggression	Death wish/thanatos	Fighting instinct
Drive theories	General affective aggression model and its related variables	Aggression machine and the point subtraction and aggression paradigm
Frustration-aggression hypothesis	Provocation	(Triggered) Displaced aggression
Rumination	Media violence	Desensitization
Excitation transfer theory	Type A/Type B behavior patterns	Hostile vs. instrumental aggression
Hostile attributional bias	Direct vs. indirect aggression	Sexual coercion
Negative-affect escape model	Bullying, bullies, victims, and bully/victims	Workplace violence vs. workplace aggression
Expressions of hostility	Obstructionism	Overt aggression
Punishment and its four conditions for success	The catharsis hypothesis	Apologies
Cognitive deficits and preattribution	The incompatible response technique	

Theoretical Perspectives on Aggression: In Search of the Roots of Violence

➤ **The Role of Biological Factors: From Instincts to the Evolutionary Psychological Perspective**

1. In your own words, define "aggression."

2. Compare and contrast how Sigmund Freud and Konrad Lorenz conceptualized aggression.

3. How would an evolutionary psychologist explain why aggression occurs?

➤ **Drive Theories: The Motive to Harm Others**

1. What is a drive theory of aggression? Identify the most famous of these theories.

> ## Modern Theories of Aggression: Taking Account of Learning, Cognitions, Mood, and Arousal

1. Identify and define the variables involved in the general affective aggression model. Be sure to label these in the order in which these occur.

Determinants of Human Aggression: Social, Personal, Situational

> ## Techniques for Studying Human Aggression: Harm without Risk?

1. Identify and discuss at least two techniques used by social psychologists in order to experimentally study aggression. Do these techniques pose any major ethical concerns?

> ## Social Determinants of Aggression: Frustration, Provocation, Displaced Aggression, Media Violence, and Heightened Arousal

1. In each of the following pairs, one of the factors is likely to produce aggression: Circle that factor.

   a.) Frustration due to fact that a person is behind schedule vs. frustration that seems illegitimate

   b.) Provocation from someone we believed meant to harm us vs. provocation from an authority figure

   c.) A mild provocation when we're having a bad day vs. a mild provocation when we're on vacation

   d.) Exposure to a violent television show vs. exposure to a nonviolent film

2. When we watch scenes of violence, we often experience _____, where we become

   hardened to the pain of others. Such viewing may also prime _____ thoughts.

3. Suppose you just found out that your sister was involved in a major car accident. In your attempt to rush to the hospital, you bump into someone who accidentally causes you to fall. On the basis of excitation transfer theory, describe the circumstances that may cause your aggression level to increase or not increase.

4. _____ sexual arousal reduces aggression because _____

   _____,while more explicit

   sexual stimuli _____

   _____. In short, the

   relationship between sexual arousal and aggression is _____.

➢ **Personal Causes of Aggression**

1. Listed below are a variety of personal causes of aggression. Your job is to detail how and why these factors are associated with aggressive tendencies.

Personal cause of aggression	How and why it's associated with aggression
Type A behavior pattern	
Hostile aggression	
Instrumental aggression	
Hostile aggression bias	
Narcissism	

2. *Boys will be boys…or will they?* For each of the scenarios below, identify whether aggression is more likely to happen with respect to men, women, or equally in both.

a.) Situations where intense provocation is present: _____

b.) Direct aggression: _____

c.) Indirect aggression: _____

d.) Sexual coercion: _____

➢ **Situational Determinants of Aggression: The Effects of High Temperature and Alcohol Consumption**

1. In contrast to those who don't consume alcohol, those who consume substantial doses of alcohol have

   been found to _____

   _____. Additionally,

   those individuals with relatively _____ tendencies to aggress become more aggressive

   when intoxicated; those with relatively _____ tendencies to aggress become

   slightly less aggressive when intoxicated.

➢ **Social Psychology: Thirty Years of Progress: Studying Heat and Aggression: From The Laboratory to Police Records of Assault**

1. Compare and contrast how social psychologists believed temperature impacted aggression thirty years ago (Then) versus the more current views on this topic (Now).
   Then   Now

➤ **Beyond The Headlines: As Social Psychologists See It...Aggression in the Air—And No Wonder!**

1. Summarize why your text authors believe that airplane travel is an experience fraught with the potential for passengers to show aggression. In the aftermath of the September eleventh disaster, do you still think this is the case?

Aggression in Long-Term Relationships: Bullying and Workplace Violence

➤ **Bullying: Singling out Others for Repeated Abuse**

1. Compare and contrast the characteristics of bullies, bully/victims, and victims.

2. Identify some practical steps to reduce bullying, particularly in school settings.

> ## Workplace Violence: Aggression on the Job

1. What is the difference between workplace violence and workplace aggression?

2. For each of the following examples, identify the category of workplace aggression involved:

   a.) Patty simply throws out memos from Tina: _____

   b.) Mark threw one of Tom's pictures off his desk in anger: _____

   c.) Polly is so disgusted by Anne's behavior that she talks behind her back whenever possible:

   _____

3. When individuals feel that they've been treated unfairly by either others in their organization or the

   organization itself, they experience _____ and often seek to

   _____. However,

   workplace aggression isn't a new or unique form of behavior; rather, it is _____

   _____.

The Prevention and Control of Aggression: Some Useful Techniques

> ## Punishment: An Effective Deterrent to Violence?

1. In your own words, what is meant by "punishment?" Under what conditions will it succeed? Given these conditions, do you think the death penalty is a "good" punishment?

> ## Catharsis: Does Getting It out of Your System Really Help?

1. *Well, does it?* Explain what the catharsis hypothesis is and then consider whether getting it out of your system is helpful.

> ## Cognitive Interventions: Apologies and Overcoming Cognitive Deficits

1. Consider how and why apologies and other procedures that help us overcome cognitive deficits (such as preattribution) often prevent aggression.

➤ Other Techniques for Reducing Aggression: Exposure to Nonaggressive Models, Training in Social Skills, and Incompatible Response

1. Complete the chart below by noting how the following techniques may help to reduce or prevent aggression.

Technique	How it works
Exposure to nonaggressive models	
Social skills training	
The incompatible response technique	

Thinking about The Aftermath of the September 11, 2001 Attacks and Aggression

I visited Ground Zero about six months after September eleventh (and I might add that it is a place that you and your family will probably want to visit someday). I had a myriad of emotions as I looked out to this massive pit where once the two tallest buildings in the world stood—and where nearly 3,000 innocent individuals were murdered. Reflecting on my visit, I was a bit surprised that I definitely felt a sense of anger after visiting Ground Zero—especially since I thought that visiting it would serve as a catharsis to me. Have you ever experienced instances when you thought that if you just "let it all out," you'd feel better—but ironically, you felt more anger or aggression? Also, what how do you think you'll feel if you visit Ground Zero *or* if you already have visited, what were your feelings?

After you read . . . Practice Tests

Practice Test 1

1. The notion that aggression stemmed from a powerful death wish was proposed by
   a. Arnold Buss.
   b. Konrad Lorenz.
   c. Sigmund Freud.
   d. Stanley Milgram.

2. Evolutionary psychologists often conceptualize (male) aggression by highlighting the importance of
   a. eliminating potential rivals for certain mates.
   b. observational learning.
   c. showcasing one's physical strength in order to boost one's self-esteem.
   d. social norms.

3. One reason why the frustration-aggression hypothesis has turned out to be largely false is that
   a. frustration does not cause aggression.
   b. aggression stems from many causes other than frustration.
   c. inconsistent with this hypothesis, aggression causes frustration, but frustration doesn't cause aggression.
   d. the importance of frustration as a predictor of aggression was greatly underestimated.

4. In the general affective aggression model, there are _____ general types of variable that impact _____ basic processes.
   a. two; two
   b. three; three
   c. two; three
   d. three; two

5. The key difference between the methodology employed by Arnold Buss versus Stanley Milgram involved the purported use of shocks is that
   a. Milgram's subjects actually administered "real" shocks to others whereas Buss' subjects did not.
   b. Milgram incorporated the use of a "teacher" and a "learner" in his study whereas Buss did not.
   c. Milgram did not give his subjects free choice about the shock level used whereas Buss did allow for free choice.
   d. Milgram, not Buss, was primarily interested in studying aggression.

6. Bob says to his co-worker Mike, "I never liked you jerk!" This is an example of
   a. displaced aggression.
   b. instrumental aggression.
   c. hostile aggression.
   d. provocation.

7. After Mark was yelled at by his wife, he screamed at his daughter just as he left his house. This scenario illustrates
   a. displaced aggression.
   b. instrumental aggression.
   c. hostile aggression.
   d. provocation.

8. After viewing a news report featuring some disturbing images of violence in the Middle East, Mary says "That's too bad—but this is to be expected in the Middle East." Mary's statement depicts the effects of
   a. prejudice.
   b. desensitization.
   c. heightened arousal.
   d. priming.

9. A key aspect of excitation transfer theory is that
   a. we tend to act aggressively when we are in a bad mood.
   b. arousal produced in one situation can persist and intensify emotional reactions in later situations.
   c. when we are overly excited, we often exhibit aggression.
   d. attributions play an essential role in determining why we sometimes show aggression.

10. Priming with sexual stimuli tends to prime
    a. aggressive thoughts in men and women.
    b. aggressive thoughts in men only.
    c. aggressive behaviors in men only.
    d. aggressive thoughts and behaviors in men only.

Practice Test 2

1. Type A individuals tend to be extremely
   a. hostile.
   b. conscientiousness.
   c. relaxed.
   d. anxious.

2. In contrast to Type B individuals, Type A individuals tend to show
   a. high levels of instrumental aggression.
   b. high levels of hostile aggression.
   c. high levels of instrumental and hostile aggression.
   d. high levels of hostile aggression and low levels of instrumental aggression.

3. Those with a hostile attributional bias are particularly apt to perceive hostile intentions in others' actions when these actions are ____.
   a. overtly aggressive
   b. ambiguous
   c. inconsequential
   d. repetitive

4. Gender differences in aggression appear to be fairly small when
   a. an individual reaches the age of fifty.
   b. an individual lives in a collectivistic society.
   c. direct aggression is involved.
   d. a provocation is present.

5. When a fight occurs in a bar, we should automatically assume that
   a. alcohol is the reason why the fight began.
   b. a factor other than alcohol caused the fight.
   c. alcohol is one of the many possible factors that contributed to the fight.
   d. the fight would not have occurred if these same individuals were in a restaurant that did not serve alcohol.

6. The hypothesis that heat increases aggression up to a point is known as the
   a. heat-aggression paradigm.
   b. temperature-anger hypothesis.
   c. negative-affect escape model.
   d. environmental-affect promotion model.

7. There tends to be a ____ relationship between heat and aggression in the ____.
   a. linear; daytime
   b. linear; night
   c. linear; day and night
   d. curvilinear; night

8. In discussing a case in which airplane passengers were trapped on the tarmac for several hours, your text authors make the point that
   a. it is inevitable that airplane travel will prime aggressive thoughts and behaviors.
   b. people can only be pushed so far before they aggress.
   c. functioning or living in extreme conditions inevitably produces aggression.
   d. individuals need to learn how to cope with difficult circumstances.

9. A defining characteristic of bullying behavior is that it only tends to occur with respect to
   a. children.
   b. individuals who know each other.
   c. prison inmates.
   d. adolescents.

10. It is fairly____ for a child to be a pure bully; also, bullying behavior tends to be found ____.
    a. uncommon; throughout the world
    b. common; throughout the world
    c. uncommon; in America only
    d. common; in America only

Practice Test 3

1. Suppose Mrs. Kerns, a fifth-grade teacher, notices two boys engaged in bullying behavior. Consequently, she should
    a. realize that bullying is a normal part of growing up.
    b. shrug off the behavior and simply conclude that 'boys will be boys.'
    c. quietly take the boys aside and ask them to cease their current behavior.
    d. bring in an outside expert to address the problem if she won't herself.

2. Workplace violence is relatively ____ and is often performed by ____.
    a. common; coworkers
    b. rare; coworkers
    c. common; outsiders
    d. rare; outsiders

3. Since Leigh is so frustrated with her co-worker Susan, she decides to launch a "whisper campaign" against her. This is an example of
    a. overt aggression.
    b. obstructionism.
    c. an expression of hostility.
    d. bullying.

4. Workplace aggression is
    a. a new, unique form of behavior.
    b. simply aggression occurring in one type of setting.
    c. overly emphasized by the media.
    d. as frequent as workplace violence.

5. If a robber believes that he'll spend six months (at most) for stealing money, then clearly the prospect of a punishment has failed to serve as a deterrent since it does *not* appear to be
    a. strong.
    b. certain.
    c. prompt.
    d. justified.

6. A layperson would tend to describe catharsis as
    a. turning inward.
    b. "holding it in."
    c. "doing your thing."
    d. "blowing off steam."

7. The catharsis hypothesis
    a. is largely correct.
    b. is partially correct.
    c. is inaccurate.
    d. remains to be tested by social psychologists.

8. Right before a faculty meeting, Iris tells one of her colleagues, "I just know that Myrna is going to explode at today's meeting—but that's just Myrna!" This example illustrates how _____ can prevent or reduce aggression.
    a. apologies
    b. preattribution
    c. repression
    d. distractions

9. Those who frequently show aggression often lack
    a. moral values.
    b. social skills.
    c. exposure to others who are aggressive.
    d. the intellectual capacity to understand why aggression is harmful.

10. In order to reduce Jake's anger, Jeff attempts to tell him a joke. Such an attempt illustrates the use of
    a. the incompatible response technique.
    b. cognitive dissonance.
    c. preattribution.
    d. anger-management training.

Comprehensive Test
(NOTE: Items 1-15 are multiple-choice questions and items 16-23 are true-false questions.)

1. Aggression is
    a. any physical harm-doing.
    b. intentional or unintentional harm-doing.
    c. inflicting harm upon others.
    d. an attitude favoring violence.

2. The instinct theory of aggression suggests that people are
    a. unlikely to engage in aggression.
    b. likely to fear aggression by instinct.
    c. biologically "programmed" for aggression.
    d. primed to learn aggression.

3. Freud believed that aggression
    a. results from the death instinct.
    b. is learned.
    c. is determined by external factors.
    d. tends to be overemphasized as a factor relating to human motivation.

4. The hypothesis that aggression increases with temperature up to a point and then drops often since it becomes uncomfortable is called the
    a. GAAM model.
    b. negative affect escape model.
    c. excitation transfer theory.
    d. drive theory of aggression.

5. Of the following, the condition that is *not* needed for punishment to deter aggression is for it to be
    a. following the aggressive act closely in time.
    b. viewed as justified by recipients.
    c. involving multiple punishments.
    d. strong.

6. Social psychologists have solved the problem of studying aggression in the laboratory by
    a. using an "aggression machine."
    b. accepting the necessity of hurting subjects.
    c. resigning themselves to study only verbal aggression.
    d. abandoning the laboratory study of aggression.

7. Suppose Henry is a Type A individual. As such, you would expect him to show all of the following characteristics, *except*
    a. hostile or irritable tendencies.
    b. always being in a hurry.
    c. being extremely competitive.
    d. insensitivity to social concerns.

8. An example of how the incompatible response technique might reduce aggression is
    a. hitting a punching bag.
    b. watching someone else be aggressive.
    c. thinking hostile thoughts.
    d. watching a funny movie.

9. The key problem with the frustration-aggression hypothesis is that frustration
   a. always leads to aggression.
   b. never leads to aggression.
   c. only intensifies aggression that is already present.
   d. can lead to other responses than aggression.

10. The main conclusion of how alcohol affects the aggressiveness of high versus low aggression individuals is that
    a. high and low aggressives increased their aggressiveness when they were intoxicated.
    b. high aggressives increased their aggressiveness when they were intoxicated.
    c. low aggressives increased their aggressiveness when they were intoxicated.
    d. alcohol consumption has no effect on aggressiveness for either.

11. Watching violent scenes may
    a. lower aggressive tendencies.
    b. prime hostile thoughts.
    c. make one more sympathetic toward the victims of violent crime.
    d. raise or lower aggression, depending on the age of the viewer.

12. Feelings of low self-esteem and perceived control coupled with high levels of Machiavellianism are associated with
    a. bullies.
    b. victims.
    c. bully/victims.
    d. bystanders to bullying.

13. In order to prevent or minimize workplace violence, organizations should try to
    a. increase salaries as frequently as possible.
    b. subject all of their employees to rigorous criminal background checks at least twice a year.
    c. address any feelings of perceived unfairness that employees may have.
    d. encourage employees to regularly update managers about "troublesome" individuals.

14. The general theme of drive theories of aggression is that
    a. genetic factors primarily explain why aggression occurs.
    b. aggression stems from external conditions that arouse a strong motive to harm others.
    c. aggression occurs, since it has proven to be adaptive over the course of evolution.
    d. internal forces, free of any external influences, cause aggression.

15. An example of ____ factor that is a determinant of human aggression would be the words or deeds of others.
    a. social
    b. personal
    c. situational
    d. genetic

16. There is considerable physical violence in the workplace.

17. The relationship between sexual arousal level and aggression is linear.

18. Heat appears to increase aggression, but only up to a point.

19. As a general rule, men always show more aggression than women.

20. A common apparatus used to measure aggression in experimental studies is the violence machine.

21. Chris has been hitting a punching bag at a gym in the hopes of "blowing off steam." As a result of this action, he should show a decrease in his overall level of aggression.

22. The frustration-aggression hypothesis is largely accepted as accurate by most contemporary social psychologists.

23. Even though a passerby in the supermarket didn't intend to knock into Ken's cart, Ken interprets this action as indicative of hostile intent. This scenario is *most* consistent with Type A behavior.

When You Have Finished . . .

TOP FIVE REASONS WHY THE STUDY OF AGGRESSION HAS GREAT RELEVANCE FOR *YOUR* LIFE

1. By understanding the nature of aggression and its causes, we are in a better position to try and prevent aggression as best as possible.

2. Inevitably though, it is often quite difficult to *not* get at least a bit upset over certain matters from time to time. By understanding some of the useful techniques to prevent and control aggression, we can try to prevent a little anger from becoming full-blown aggression.

3. We should mindful of the situational determinants of aggression and try to avoid these situational influences as much as possible.

4. We should be mindful of the personality-based determinants of aggression and, if we exhibit such characteristics (e.g., Type A behavior), then we should make a conscious effort to alter this aspect of our personality.

5. We should realize the particularly harmful effects of aggression in long-term relationships, particularly as it applies to bullying and workplace violence. In doing so, let us strive to make the workplace and the worlds of our children as pleasant as they possibly be.

Let's revisit point #5. Think back to your childhood and adolescence. Can you still identify which of your peers were bullies, bully/victims, or victims? In which category did *you* find yourself? Were the characteristics of these three types of individuals that you knew consistent with the characteristics of bullies, bully/victims, or victims as discussed in your text? Did anyone (e.g., a teacher or parent) help to end the bullying? Now, as a parent or a potential parent (in the years ahead), how do *you* think you would work to prevent bullying behavior with respect to your own children and their peers?

Short Answer/Essay Questions

1. **Theories of Aggression**
   State the two main categories of variables in the general affective aggression model and give a couple of examples of each.

2. **Personal Causes of Aggression**
   Define the three main characteristics of the Type A behavior pattern.

3. **Alcohol and Aggression**
   Discuss how alcohol affects aggression for those who are low or high aggressors.

4. **Aggression in the Workplace**
   Briefly describe the three major categories of aggression in the workplace.

➤ **Social Psychology: Thirty Years of Progress...From Drive to Attentional Focus: How Does the Presence of Others Influence Task Performance?**

1. Compare and contrast how social psychologists studied social facilitation thirty years ago (Then) versus the more current views on this topic (Now). Be sure to contrast the drive theory of social facilitation with distraction-conflict theory as part of your response.

<u>Then</u>   <u>Now</u>

➤ **Social Loafing: Letting Others Do the Work When Part of a Group**

1. In your own words, define the terms, "additive tasks" and "social loafing."

2. How does the collective effort model explain why social loafing occurs?

3. Identify the five conditions when social loafing effects will be the weakest, as well as practical ways to reduce social loafing.

Coordination in Groups: Cooperation or Conflict?

> ## Cooperation: Working with Others to Achieve Shared Goals

1. Contrast the patterns of behavior shown with respect to cooperation and conflict.

2. Explain what is meant by a "social dilemma." Also, identify the possible steps that a person can take under such a condition.

3. State the three key factors that influence cooperation.

4. What is the discontinuity effect and why does it occur?

➤ **Beyond The Headlines: As Social Psychologists See It…"We're All in This Together, So Why Doesn't Everyone Do Their Share?": A Social Dilemma in the Office**

1. According to your text authors, why is it that most people are reluctant to clean the office refrigerator? Do you agree with their views?

➤ **Conflict: Its Nature, Causes, and Effects**

1. State the four key elements in conflict.

2. Complete the chart below by listing the four main causes and characteristics of conflict.

Factor	Characteristics

➤ Cooperation: Working with Others to Achieve Shared Goals

1. List three tactics used to reduce an opponent's aspirations.

2. List four tactics that are ethically questionable.

3. What is the difference between an "integrative agreement" and "superordinate goals?"

➤ Conflict across Ethnic and Cultural Boundaries

1. Cross-cultural conflicts are especially difficult to resolve because people tend to focus on _____

_____ and *not* _____

_____.

Perceived Fairness in Groups: Its Nature and Effects

➤ Cooperation: Working with Others to Achieve Shared Goals

1. Match it! Match each phrase, word, or sentence on the left side of the page with an identifying concept on the right side of the page. Note that each item on the right should be used *only once*.

   ___1. Individual judgment as to whether they've received their   A. procedural justice
       fair share of rewards

   ___2. Fair procedures used to distribute available rewards   B. interactional justice

   ___3. Courtesy shown by those who distribute rewards   C. distributive justice

2. Suppose you received a "D" on a paper for which you were expecting at least a "B" and decide to speak with your professor about this matter. Under what conditions would you probably *not* feel a sense of interactional justice?

➤ Reactions to Perceived Unfairness: Tactics for Dealing with Injustice

1. Summarize how the issue of perceived unfairness factors into romantic relationships, particularly marriages.

Decision Making by Groups: How It Occurs and the Pitfalls It Faces

➢ **The Decision-Making Process: How Groups Attain Consensus**

1. In your own words, define "decision making."

2. Name that social decision scheme! Actually, first define a "social decision scheme:"

   Now, consider the following hypothetical scenarios and identify the social decision scheme under use:

   a.) After a group has been deadlocked as how to resolve the company's financial matter, a member simply says "Why don't we just cut back on our spending?" At that point, the group agrees to go with this suggestion.

   b.) After spending many days arguing which job candidate should get the job position, a group member says "Listen, the majority of us felt that Jeff was the best candidate from the outset of our discussions, so I say we go with Jeff." After hearing this statement, the committee decides to offer the job to Jeff.

   c.) After Anna suggests to her colleagues that it is important to reconsider her company's dress code, more and more members of her group agree with this position.

3. Explain how normative and informational social influence can cause individuals to go along with the group.

➤ The Nature of Group Decisions: Moderation or Polarization?

1.a. Suppose a group of war veterans get together for their monthly meeting. They begin discussing their views on whether America is too involved in worldwide affairs. Their average view is represented by an "X" below. After they're done talking, place an "X" on the scale that will likely represent their average view on this issue once they're done talking.

	X	
1	5	10
America is too involved	Moderate	America isn't involved enough

b. Name and define the phenomenon that the above example illustrates. Why does it occur?

➤ Potential Dangers of Group Decision Making: Groupthink, Biased Processing, and the Tendency of Group Members to Tell Each Other What They Already Know

1. What is "groupthink" and why does it occur? Identify at least two ways that faulty group decision making, such as groupthink, can be avoided and improved.

Thinking about The Aftermath of the September 11, 2001 Attacks and Group Behavior

At the time of this writing, there remains many unanswered questions regarding the war on terrorism, such as how to resolve the Israeli-Arab conflict and whether to wage war against Iraq. Clearly, many governments around the world have many critical decisions to make in the months and years ahead. Given what you now know about some of the pitfalls of group behavior, such as groupthink and group polarization, what advice what you give policy makers in America and other countries if you were able to?

After you read . . . Practice Tests

Practice Test 1

1. A collection of persons who are perceived to be bonded together in a coherent unit are called a(n)
   a. group.
   b. class.
   c. chunked unit.
   d. organization.

2. Of the following, _____ are considered to have the *least* amount of entiativity.
   a. people attending an athletic contest
   b. people in line at a bank
   c. members of a labor union
   d. women

3. Matthew is a Jewish-American who belongs to a certain synagogue. The type of group to which he belongs would be classified as a(n) ____.
   a. intimacy group
   b. weak social relationship
   c. task-oriented group
   d. social category

4. Harry belongs to an astronomy society where he is the co-president. As such, he appears to have much ____ within the group.
   a. status
   b. role conflict
   c. cohesiveness
   d. norm-related behavior

5. Adherence to norms within a group often leads to
   a. decreased cohesiveness.
   b. role conflict.
   c. increased status.
   d. profound difficulties for the group.

6. A key reason why cohesiveness develops in groups is due to
   a. genuine liking.
   b. destructive obedience.
   c. depersonalized attraction.
   d. the lack of external threats.

7. Early research by Allport (1920) found that when others were present, performance was
   a. enhanced.
   b. weakened.
   c. unchanged.
   d. enhanced only if the individual personally knew the other individuals who were present.

8. According to Zajonc's drive theory of social facilitation, the main reason why social facilitation occurs is due to
   a. social desirability concerns.
   b. self-efficacy.
   c. a desire to show off in front of others.
   d. arousal generated from the mere presence of others.

9. Zajonc and colleagues (1969) found that ____ were more able to complete a ____ maze when in the presence of other ____.
   a. roaches; simple; roaches
   b. roaches; complex; roaches
   c. college students; simple; college students
   d. college students; complex; college students

10. Distraction-conflict theory suggests that audiences produce social facilitation effects only when
    a. we believe that we are being critically judged by them.
    b. directing attention to them conflicts in some way with task demands.
    c. we feel unprepared to perform.
    d. it is in our own best interest to do so.

Practice Test 2

1. The end result of working with others on a project, rather than working individually, is that working with others tends to cause individuals to
   a. work harder.
   b. purposely create problems.
   c. make errors.
   d. reduce their effort.

2. Social loafing effects tend to *not* occur with respect to ____.
   a. men
   b. women.
   c. individualistic cultures
   d. collectivistic cultures

3. ____ refers to a belief that better performance will be recognized and rewarded.
   a. Expectancy
   b. Instrumentality
   c. Valence
   d. Justice

4. Anthony owns a construction company and has noticed a great deal of social loafing. He can reduce this by
   a. making the output of each person readily identifiable.
   b. minimizing group members' commitment to successful task performance.
   c. downplaying the relative importance of a task.
   d. emphasizing that each workers' task is not unique.

5. All of the following terms are associated with the concept of conflict, *except*
   a. process.
   b. incompatible.
   c. negative results.
   d. shared

6. In the prisoner's dilemma, the greatest risk for a given individual occurs when the individual ____ action and his or her counterpart ____ takes action.
   a. does not; does not
   b. does; does
   c. does not; does
   d. does; does not

7. Reciprocal altruism appears to have ____ evolutionary benefits.
   a. great
   b. minimal
   c. no
   d. negative

8. Your text authors conclude that the key reason why many individuals are reluctant to clean the office refrigerator is due to
   a. social loafing.
   b. "free riders."
   c. the dynamics of a social dilemma.
   d. the discontinuity effect.

9. Suppose Sally is facing a social dilemma of some sort and she focuses primarily on defeating others. Consequently, she appears to have a ____ orientation.
   a. competitive
   b. vindictive
   c. cooperative
   d. individualistic

10. The discontinuity effect refers to the
    a. greater tendency for groups instead of individuals to compete in mixed-motive situations.
    b. greater tendency for individuals instead of groups to compete in mixed-motive situations.
    c. general tendency for a consortium to show intergroup cooperation.
    d. finding that intragroup and intergroup cooperation is equally likely to occur.

Practice Test 3

1. The key elements of conflict include all of the following, *except*
   a. opposing interests between individuals or groups.
   b. recognition of opposition by relevant parties.
   c. the belief by each side that the other will act to interfere with these interests.
   d. the lack of specific actions that produce interferences for the parties.

2. Suppose Harriet dislikes Roz since she believes that Roz thwarted her efforts to get a raise at work. The major source of conflict in this case is likely
    a. a faulty attribution.
    b. faulty communication.
    c. the status quo bias.
    d. Harriet's Type A behavior.

3. The ____ tactic for reaching integrative agreements involves increasing available resources so that both sides can obtain their major goals.
    a. logrolling
    b. broadening the pie
    c. bridging
    d. cost cutting

4. Superordinate goals tend to
    a. create conflict.
    b. allow opposing groups to find a way to end their conflict by considering mutual interests.
    c. highlight differences between groups.
    d. hinder overt cooperation.

5. Heather decided to complain to her college dean about the manner in which her professor decided to handle grades in her class. As such, she appears to be *most* concerned with ____.
    a. distributive justice
    b. procedural justice
    c. interpersonal justice
    d. equitable justice

6. In marriages, perceived unfairness is
    a. the result of marital conflict (only).
    b. the cause of marital conflict (only).
    c. a potential result and cause of marital conflict.
    d. only of concern for women.

7. Suppose Joe is considered to be a "maverick" who won't follow the group's general views. In order to try to bring Joe into line, one of the group members presents data that supposedly contradicts Joe's beliefs. In this example, ____ is being used in order to attain consensus.
    a. informational social influence
    b. normative social influence
    c. the first-shift rule
    d. the truth-wins rule

8. ____ has (have) contributed to major historical blunders or disasters.
    a. Only group polarization
    b. Only groupthink
    c. Group polarization and groupthink
    d. Neither group polarization nor groupthink

9. If a jury was engaged in biased processing, then its members were likely
   a. attempting to ascertain whether any of the witnesses had a bias of some sort.
   b. refusing to comply with the judge's order.
   c. processing information in ways that allowed them to reach the decision they wanted.
   d. exhibiting groupthink.

10. Suppose Kathy says that she profoundly disagrees with the strategy that her co-workers appear to be in favor of adopting. Assuming that she wasn't instructed to make such a disagreement, her behavior illustrates ____.
    a. groupthink.
    b. the devil's advocate technique.
    c. authentic dissent.
    d. group polarization.

Comprehensive Test

(NOTE: Items 1-15 are multiple-choice questions and items 16-23 are true-false questions.)

1. Tom, Mary, and Sue are all part of a group where they are expected to accomplish different tasks for the group. This illustrates the importance of ____ in groups.
   a. status
   b. norms
   c. roles
   d. cohesiveness

2. If group members like each other and are united in pursuit of the group's goals, they are expressing a high amount of ____.
   a. cohesiveness
   b. groupthink
   c. interpersonal attraction
   d. cooperation

3. According to Zajonc's drive theory of social facilitation, the presence of others produces an increase in
   a. confidence.
   b. self-motivated interest.
   c. arousal.
   d. empathy.

4. Which of the following statements *best* describes social loafing?
   a. When people are doing a task, they work harder when getting paid for it.
   b. When people are doing a task, they work harder when it's their own project than one they've been assigned.
   c. When people work together on a joint task, each member exerts less effort than when they work alone.
   d. When people are doing a task, they work harder when being watched.

5. Judgments of distributive justice require that individuals perceive fairness in the
    a. procedures used to divide rewards among group members.
    b. considerateness and courtesy shown by those who divide available rewards.
    c. ratio of contributions to outcomes for themselves and for others in the group.
    d. outcomes they personally receive without regard to what others get.

6. ____ pertains to the considerateness and courtesy shown to group members by those responsible for distributing available awards.
    a. Distributive justice
    b. Procedural justice
    c. Interpersonal justice
    d. Equitable justice

7. The ____ rule suggests that the correct solution will ultimately be accepted by the group as its correctness is recognized by more and more members.
    a. social-comparison
    b. truth-wins
    c. majority-wins
    d. first-shift

8. Suppose a group composed of individuals who moderately approve of gambling get together to exchange their shared views. Group polarization would predict that after some discussion their views will likely be
    a. more extreme than the views they initially held.
    b. less extreme than the views they initially held.
    c. no different than the views they initially held.
    d. quite divided.

9. All of the following are determinants of groupthink, *except*
    a. leadership that is concerned with hearing all group members' views.
    b. a high level of cohesiveness among group members.
    c. pressure to maintain a high level of group consensus.
    d. group norms preventing a consideration of alternate courses of action.

10. Research on the pooling of information during group decision making suggests that group members are more likely to discuss ____ information and that this tendency ____ that groups will make the best decisions.
    a. shared; assures
    b. shared; jeopardizes
    c. unshared; assures
    d. unshared; jeopardizes

11. Situations where individuals can potentially enhance their own individuals outcomes by acting in a particular way are referred to as ____.
    a. social dilemmas.
    b. negative frames.
    c. reciprocal conflicts.
    d. incompatible bargains.

12. ____ is a basic rule of social life suggesting that individuals tend to return the kind of treatment they have previously received from others.
    a. Cooperation
    b. Framing
    c. Distributive justice
    d. Reciprocity

13. When we believe that a group is ____ in entiativity, we tend to compare the group members with ____.
    a. low; each other
    b. high; each other
    c. low; other groups
    d. high; each other

14. It is often possible to acquire social status within a group by displaying
    a. indifference.
    b. sadness.
    c. overt rage.
    d. quiet anger.

15. All of the following are examples of ethically questionable ways to resolve conflict, *except*
    a. attacking an opponent's network.
    b. misrepresentation.
    c. making false promises.
    d. adopting superordinate goals.

16. Social facilitation occurs in humans and other species.

17. Distributive justice pertains to whether a person believes that he or she has been treated fairly in a group and with courtesy and considerateness.

18. An additive task refers to group members' contributions combined into a single group output.

19. Social loafing is enhanced when a person works with others he or she doesn't respect.

20. The rules within a group telling members how they should behave are called roles.

21. Suppose a group of conservatives get together to talk about a host of issues. At the conclusion of their discussions, they find that their views have become even more conservative. This example illustrates groupthink.

22. The social decision scheme that serves to strengthen the initially most popular view is the truth-wins rule.

23. Groupthink has *not* been shown to have any negative consequences with respect to major, historical decisions.

When You Have Finished . . .

TOP TEN REASONS WHY THE STUDY OF GROUPS HAS GREAT RELEVANCE FOR *YOUR* LIFE

1. Virtually all of us at any given point in our lives is part of a group, whether it be at work, school, as part of a sports team, or a myriad of other possibilities. As such, we should all be interested in how to make these interactions as productive and pleasant as possible for all parties concerned.

2. Sometimes groups make devastating inaccurate decisions, often as a result of groupthink or group polarization. By being aware of these pitfalls, *you* may be in a position to help steer your particular group away from such faulty decisions.

3. Unfortunately, conflict often arises in groups—but it doesn't have to be a reality. The next time you face a conflict within or between groups, consider using some of the techniques outlined in your text.

4. Even though social loafing is quite common, there are ways to lessen its occurrence. The next time you have a group project of some sort, keep in mind some of the tips for reducing social loafing as discussed in your text.

5. Since we often have to make presentations or performances to others, try to use the research on social facilitation to *your* advantage by noting when and how to maximize your performance.

Revisit points #3 and 4 by thinking about previous or current group situations involving conflict or social loafing that you've experienced. To what degree where the techniques that were outlined in your text helpful in dealing with these problems or issues?

Short Answer/Essay Questions

1. **How Groups Function**
   Briefly outline the four key factors that allow groups to function.

2. **Social Loafing**
Provide an overview of the key predictions from expectancy-valence theory.

3. **Conflict**
State and describe three major social factors that play an important role in terms of causing conflict.

4. **Judgments of Fairness**
The Dean at a public university rewards faculty with pay bonuses as a function to each individual's contributions to the school. What type of justice does this example *best* illustrate?

5. **Decision-Making Processes**
State and define three social decision schemes.

13 SOCIAL PSYCHOLOGY IN ACTION: APPLICATIONS TO LAW, MEDICINE, AND ORGANIZATIONS

Before you read . . .

The final chapter of your text looks at how social psychological research has been applied to three key "real world" areas: law, medicine/health, and organizations/the workplace. You'll first consider some central issues to forensic psychology, which has to do with the psychological study of legal issues. For instance, you'll have a good understanding of why sometimes the outcome of a trial is greatly determined by what happens *before* the trial ever begins. You'll also understand why eyewitness testimony is often faulty and how it can be improved. A discussion of how the central participants of a trial (i.e., judges, attorneys, jurors, and defendants) help to shape the verdict will also featured. After that, you'll be exposed to the fascinating and ever-developing field of health psychology. As part of this discussion, you'll find out about the factors that shape our responses to health-related information and how to deal with the harmful effects of stress. The last segment of this chapter considers industrial/organizational psychology. You will learn that this field, which examines the psychology of organizations and workplace, considers such issues as job satisfaction, why we show helpful behaviors at work, and various styles and characteristics of leadership.

Chapter Objectives

After reading this chapter, you should be able to:

- Identify and contrast the issues studied by a forensic, health, and industrial-organizational psychologist.

- Outline the effects that police procedures (including interrogations leading to the "recovery" of repressed memories) and the media may have on the general impact of a trial before it begins.

- Consider why eyewitness testimony is often faulty and identify ways to improve such recall.

- Consider how certain tactics and behaviors by attorneys and judges may influence a jury.

- Identify some of the key characteristics of defendants and jurors that help to predict how a juror may vote in a court case.

- Discuss how we may respond to health-related information.

- Provide an overview of the physical and psychological consequences of stress.

- Contrast the disease-prone personality with the self-healing personality.

- Describe how increased fitness, positive emotions and regulatory control, and social support can help individuals cope with stress.

- Contrast some of the key organizational and personal factors that seem to predict job satisfaction.

- Define what is meant by "organizational citizenship behavior" and why it occurs.

- Discuss the great person theory of leadership and identify some of the key characteristics of leaders.

- Contrast the two basic dimensions of leader behavior.

- Compare and contrast the following leadership styles: transformational, democratic, autocratic, laissez-faire, and transactional.

As you read . . .

Remember this! Below are a list of some of the key terms and concepts from this chapter. Make flashcards in order to enhance your recall ability of these terms. Refer to the definitions that are either in boldface or in the margins of this chapter for help. Be advised that you may also want to include additional terms from this chapter as you deem necessary.

Forensic psychology	Repressed memory/psychogenic amnesia	Eyewitness testimony and factors that influence its accuracy
Blank-lineup control	Voir dire	Leading questions
Need for cognition	Examples of juror characteristics	Health psychology
Positively vs. negatively framed message	Unrealistic optimism/optimistic bias	Social-image concern
Stress	Coping	Psychoneuroimmunology
Secretory immunoglobulin A	Disease-prone vs. self-healing personality	Fitness
Emotion- vs. problem-solving coping	Regulatory control	Social support
Industrial/organizational psychology	Job satisfaction	Organizational commitment
Core self-evaluations	Affective temperament	Organizational citizenship behavior
Leadership	The great person theory	The traits of leaders
The Big Five dimensions of personality	Initiating structure	Consideration

| Transformational leaders and their characteristics | The three leadership styles identified by Lewin and colleagues | Transactional leaders |

Applying Social Psychology to the Interpersonal Aspects of the Legal System

➤ **Before the Trial Begins: Effects of Police Procedures and Media Coverage**

1. In your own words, discuss the issues considered by a "forensic psychologist."

2. How do detectives go about the interrogation process?

3. When we try to remember any event or past experience, the result is _____

   _____.

4. When telling their stories to the police, suspects and witnesses have three expectations about the police officers' expectations. Name these!

5. Explain what is meant by a "repressed memory" and "psychogenic amnesia." Do you think we can ever truly forget an event?

6. Even though most crime rates have dropped in the U.S., people still claim great concern about being a victim of crime. What might account for this fear?

7. Summarize what typically occurs when a criminal case receives a lot of pretrial publicity.

➤ **Eyewitness Testimony: Problems and Solutions**

1. It's debate time again! Listed below are a series of points. Your job is to refute these points by offering your own counterpoint.

   Point: *Eyewitness testimony is fairly accurate.*

   Counterpoint:

   Point: *Eyewitness testimony is only inaccurate is when a person has a reason to lie.*

   Counterpoint:

Point: *There are very few factors that influence eyewitness accuracy.*

Counterpoint:

Point: *Experienced police officers can easily identify a suspect accused of committing a crime caught on videotape.*

Counterpoint:

Point: *There simply is nothing that can be done about increasing the accuracy of eyewitness testimony.*

Counterpoint:

➤ The Central Participants in a Trial: Effects of Attorneys, Judges, Jurors, and Defendants

1. Explain the voir dire procedure.

2. Define a "leading question" and when these are allowed to be asked. In reality though, does this always happen the way it should according to the law?

3. A juror with _____ may *not* always follow a judge's orders to ignore certain parts of courtroom testimony.

4. Discuss how jurors tend to respond when they believe that the judge feels that the defendant is guilty versus innocent.

5. Create a list of key juror and defendant characteristics and the impact these have on the verdict.

Juror or Defendant Characteristic?	Description of Characteristic	Impact on Verdict

Applying Social Psychology to Health-Related Behavior

➤ **Responding to Health-Related Information**

1. Health psychology is _____

   _____.

2 Match it! Match each phrase, word, or sentence on the left side of the page with an identifying concept on the right side of the page. Note that each item on the right should be used *only once*.

    ___1. Concerns about what others think may color   A. positively framed message
             processing of health information

    ___2. Effective in motivating detection behavior message   B. negatively framed message

    ___3. Associated with ignoring health messages   C. social-image concern

    ___4. Effective in motivating preventive behavior   D. optimistic bias

➤ **Responding to Health-Related Information**

1. In your own words, what does it mean to "cope with stress?"

2. Complete this chart by listing: a) events that could cause stress, b) the psychological effects of stress, and c) the physiological consequences of stress.

Stressful events	Psychological effects	Physiological effects

253

3. Compare and contrast the differences between the self-healing and disease-prone personality.

➤ Coping with Stress

1. Suppose Steve is so stressed about his work that he feels like he is the target for criticism from his boss at any moment as depicted in the picture below. Outline ways he can cope with his stress by discussing the role of increased fitness, emotion- and problem-focused coping, social support, and any other ways that may be beneficial to reducing his (or your) stress level.

➤ Beyond The Headlines: As Social Psychologists See It…Pets Can Help Reduce Stress

1. Why do your text authors maintain that "pet therapy" can reduce stress? Do you agree?

Applying Social Psychology to the World of Work: Job Satisfaction, Helping, and Leadership

---

➤ ## Job Satisfaction: Attitudes about Work

1. Discuss the issues of concern to an industrial/organizational psychologist.

2. List some organizational and personal factors related to satisfaction.

3. Why do your text authors conclude that "some individuals have a tendency to express either relatively high or relatively low levels of job satisfaction *no matter where they work?"*

➤ ## Organizational Citizenship Behavior: Prosocial Behavior at Work

1. What is "organizational citizenship behavior" and why does it occur?

➢ **Leadership Patterns of Influence within Groups**

1. What is the great person theory of leadership? What characteristics do leaders possess? Which of these are the *most* important?

2. List the Big Five dimensions of personality and explain what each of these dimensions has to do with leadership.

3. Complete the following chart by listing the key characteristics associated with an initiating structure, consideration, and transformational leadership.

Initiating structure	Consideration	Transformational leadership

Practice Test 3

1. Attitudes toward one's company are known as
   a. job satisfaction.
   b. organizational commitment.
   c. organizational citizenship behavior.
   d. career happiness.

2. A personal factor related to job satisfaction is
   a. seniority.
   b. liking one's boss.
   c. a perception that reward systems are fair.
   d. when employees are underloaded with work.

3. The relationship between job satisfaction and task performance is ____.
   a. not significant.
   b. relatively weak.
   c. (surprisingly) inversely related.
   d. extremely strong.

4. An example of ____ would be helping others who have a heavy workload.
   a. affective temperament
   b. transformational leadership
   c. consideration
   d. organizational citizenship behavior

5. A key premise behind the great person theory of leadership is that great leaders are
   a. made, not born.
   b. incapable of being truly understood.
   c. quite different from most others in terms of the traits they possess.
   d. greatly flawed in their personal life.

6. ____ is considered to be one of the Big Five dimensions of personality.
   a. Conscientiousness
   b. Consciousness
   c. Kindness
   d. Psychoticism

7. Leaders who are ____ on the dimension of initiating structure tend to be considered with production and leaders who are ____ on the dimension of consideration tend to unconcerned with people.
   a. high; high
   b. low; low
   c. high; low
   d. low; high

8. Suppose Peter is viewed by his followers as a transformational leader in that he is a charismatic role model. As such, this example highlights the importance of _____ in transformational leadership.
    a. intellectual stimulation
    b. inspirational motivation
    c. individual consideration
    d. idealized influence

9. According to Lewin and colleagues (1939), a(n) _____ leadership style is ideal since it encourages a high level of productivity and cooperation among group members.
    a. transformational
    b. transactional
    c. democratic
    d. autocratic

10. Leaders who are high in charisma tend to be well suited for environments that are
    a. stable and predictable.
    b. chaotic and rapidly changing.
    c. stable or chaotic.
    d. not in the "for-profit" business sector.

Comprehensive Test
(NOTE: Items 1-15 are multiple-choice questions and items 16-23 are true-false questions.)

1. Media information influences the public
    a. in surprisingly few instances.
    b. when negative aspects of the suspect are mentioned.
    c. when positive aspects of the suspect are mentioned.
    d. by making them it favorable to the defense argument.

2. Wells and Luus (1990) argue that a police lineup is analogous to a
    a. social psychology experiment.
    b. beauty contest.
    c. wrestling match.
    d. game show.

3. In terms of their ability to select jurors favorable to their side, attorneys are
    a. better than non-attorneys.
    b. uniformly skilled.
    c. uniformly dismal.
    d. no better than college students in doing so.

4. In American courtrooms, leading questions are ____ .
   a. never permitted
   b. permitted when the witness is first examined
   c. permitted upon cross-examination
   d. permitted throughout any trial

5. Jurors who are ____ tend to comply selectively with instructions about inadmissibility.
   a. extraverted
   b. high in the need for cognition
   c. low in the need for cognition
   d. low in agreeableness

6. ____ is associated with ignoring various health messages.
   a. Optimism
   b. Unrealistic optimism
   c. Pessimism
   d. Unrealistic pessimism

7. Suppose you're at a party and someone you don't know well says, "Here's some beer—just to let you know, I took a swig from that cup." Based on this information only, you'll likely drink that beer if you have
   a. alcohol myopia.
   b. an optimism bias.
   c. a low social image concern.
   d. a high social image concern.

8. ____ refers to how we deal with threats and their emotional consequences.
   a. Stress
   b. Coping
   c. Psychological response
   d. Psychoneurimmunology

9. Suppose George, who was a pessimist, had an untimely death at age forty due to a heart attack. In terms of understanding why George died relatively early, his pessimism
   a. definitely played no role whatsoever.
   b. definitely caused his heart attack.
   c. may have served as a contributing factor.
   d. probably made him feel anger and anxious while he was alive, but it likely didn't contribute to his heart attack.

10. Holly tends to respond to stress with intensely negative emotions and tends to be sick a great deal. Based on this information, Holly probably exhibits a
    a. Type A behavior pattern.
    b. disease-prone personality.
    c. low social image concern.
    d. high level of psychoneuroimmunology.

11. Industrial-organizational psychology is a branch of
    a. business dominated by psychology.
    b. psychology that dominates the mindset of major corporate businesses.
    c. law that specializes in psychological matters.
    d. psychology that studies behavior in work settings.

12. In terms of its impact on job satisfaction, genetics
    a. plays a very insignificant role.
    b. plays a very important role such that some people will have high or low levels of job satisfaction, no matter where they work.
    c. only predicts what our professions will be and not our levels of job satisfaction.
    d. has not been considered yet as a potential factor related to job satisfaction.

13. All of the following factors may explain why a person engages in various forms of OCB, *except*
    a. a narrow perception of the roles of one's job.
    b. job loyalty.
    c. a hope to be rewarded for such behavior.
    d. feelings of perceived justice.

14. The single most important characteristic of leaders is
    a. motivation.
    b. drive.
    c. flexibility.
    d. self-confidence.

15. All of the following leadership styles were identified by Lewin and colleagues (1939), *except*
    a. transactional.
    b. autocratic.
    c. democratic.
    d. laissez-faire.

16. Even though social support may make a person feel good, it does *not* help individuals cope with an illness.

17. Negatively framed messages work best for promoting detection behavior.

18. The "disease prone personality" only refers to physical or physiological health risks.

19. The stated purpose of voir dire is to ensure that fair and impartial jurors are selected.

20. A defendant's race rarely figures into a jury's final verdict.

21. Some individuals may show the same level of job satisfaction regardless of where they work.

22. A worker's trust in their boss and company is unrelated to their organizational citizenship behavior.

23. Most individuals are quite wary and distrustful of charismatic leaders.

When You Have Finished . . .

TOP TEN REASONS WHY SOCIAL PSYCHOLOGY APPLICATIONS TO LAW, MEDICINE, AND ORGNAIZATIONS HAS GREAT RELEVANCE FOR *YOUR* LIFE

1. Any time social psychologists try to *apply* their findings, this has an inherent value and relevance to our everyday lives.

2. Since we all must encounter stress at varying levels and times in our lives, we need to find ways to effectively cope with it.

3. If you ever witness a crime, become a crime victim, or serve as a juror, having an awareness of the psychology of the legal system might allow for you to provide the most objective information possible.

4. By understanding the factors that influence job satisfaction, we are in a better position to maximize our satisfaction with our chosen job or career.

5. By understanding patterns of leadership, you'll have a better understanding of how your boss operates—or, if you're in a leadership position, you'll be aware of what makes an effective leader.

With respect to point #2, consider some of the suggestions outlined in your text as to how to manage and cope with stress (e.g., increased fitness and social support). The next time you find yourself in a stressful situation, try one or more of these techniques and keep a diary of some sort to note the effectiveness of these techniques in combating stress. Were some techniques more effective than others? Which ones? Were certain techniques effective under certain conditions only? If so, how?

Short Answer/Essay Questions

1. **Eyewitness Testimony**
   Briefly identify two or three ways to increase and improve eyewitness accuracy.

2. **The Impact of Stress**
   Provide at least two examples of how stress can directly cause physical illness.

3. **Social Support**
   Explain why social support can sometimes provide more harm than good to an individual.

4. **Organizational Citizenship Behavior (OCB)**
   How is the issue of perceived justice relevant to the occurrence of OCB?

5. **Leadership Styles**
   Discuss how important it is to have a charismatic leader during stable versus changing times or environments.

CHAPTER ANSWERS: "AFTER YOU READ" PRACTICE TESTS AND SHORT ANSWER/ESSAY QUESTIONS

Chapter 1

Item Number	Practice Test 1	Practice Test 2	Practice Test 3	Comprehensive Test
1	B (p. 6)	B (p. 5)	A (p. 24)	A (p. 5)
2	A (p. 18)	A (p. 9)	C (p. 26)	C (p. 6)
3	D (p. 30)	C (p. 12)	B (p. 28)	C (pp. 7-8)
4	A (p. 22)	B (p. 10)	B (p. 30)	C (p. 11)
5	A (p. 24)	D (p. 15)	C (p. 15)	C (p. 12)
6	C (p. 27)	B (p. 18)	D (p. 18)	A (p. 14)
7	B (p. 27)	D (p. 20)	D (p. 20)	D (p. 18)
8	C (p. 29)	A (p. 20)	A (p. 24)	B (p. 17)
9	D (p. 30)	C (p. 21)	C (p. 27)	D (p. 21)
10	C (p. 31)	C (pp. 23-24)	C (p. 28)	B (p. 22)
11				B (p. 24)
12				C (p. 27)
13				A (pp. 28-29)
14				D (p. 30)
15				D (p. 31)
16				F (pp. 5-6)
17		*Correct Responses to*		T (p. 8)
18		*Short Answer/Essay Questions*		F (p. 8)
19				F (pp. 10-11)
20		↓		F (p. 18)
21				T (p. 22)
22				F (p. 28)
23				F (p. 30)

1. The four most important core values to a scientific field are: accuracy, objectivity, skepticism, and open-mindedness. (p. 6)

2. The three basic processes of evolution are: variation, inheritance, and selection. Variation refers to the fact that organisms belonging to a given species vary in many different ways. Inheritance pertains to how these variations are passed from one generation to the next through complex mechanisms.

Selection refers to the fact that some of these variations give individuals an "edge" in terms of reproduction. (p. 12)

3. Based on this negative correlation coefficient value of -.43, the more a person argues with his or her friend (on average), the number of colds a person reports (on average per year) decreases. Obviously, causality cannot be determined given the correlational nature of this study. (p. 20)

4. The independent variable would be the issue that the subjects wrote about (i.e., either the benefits or drawbacks to their relationship or what they ate for breakfast); the dependent variable would be the subject's blood pressure. (p. 22)

5. Deception is often used in social psychological research since participants' behavior might be altered if they knew the true purposes of a study; thus, valid information about social behavior or thought wouldn't be gained. Two problems associated with deception are harm to the subjects or a negative attitude about (social) psychology and research. In order to minimize these problems, social psychologists should never try to use deception to persuade individuals to participate in studies. They should also try to use informed consent and debriefing in all studies. (pp. 29-31)

Chapter 2

Item Number	Practice Test 1	Practice Test 2	Practice Test 3	Comprehensive Test
1	A (p. 39)	D (p. 38)	D (pp. 38-39)	A (p. 39)
2	C (p. 41)	C (p. 40)	B (p. 45)	C (p. 40)
3	B (p. 42)	B (p. 41)	C (p. 50)	A (p. 41)
4	C (p. 44)	A (p. 52)	B (p. 51)	D (p. 42)
5	B (p. 49)	B (p. 53)	C (pp. 52-53)	B (pp. 45-46)
6	A (p. 52)	C (p. 56)	B (p. 54)	C (pp. 47-48)
7	B (p. 59)	D (p. 58)	D (p. 58)	A (pp. 50-51)
8	D (pp. 62-63)	B (p. 34)	C (p. 59)	A (pp. 52-53)
9	C (p. 65)	A (p. 69)	B (p. 65)	B (p. 53)
10	B (p. 69)	D (pp. 71-72)	A (pp. 70-71)	D (p. 56)
11				A (p. 56)
12				A (pp. 57-58)
13				A (p. 59)
14				C (pp. 61-62)
15		*Correct Responses to Short Answer/Essay Questions* ↓		D (p. 69)
16				T (p. 40)
17				F (pp. 40-41)
18				T (p. 45)
19				T (pp. 50-51)
20				T (pp. 52-53)
21				F (p. 58)
22				F (pp. 61-62)
23				T (p. 68)

[continued on next page]

CHAPTER ANSWERS

1. Three nonverbal cues related to deception are: microexpressions, interchannel discrepancies, and exaggerated facial expressions. Review page 45 of your text for more detailed definitions of these cues and additional ones.

2. We would tend to conclude that this person is generally a loud and inconsiderate person, according to Jones and Davis' theory. The reason is that it represents freely chosen behavior that is not social desirable and it yields distinctive, noncommon effects. (pp. 50-51)

3. Clearly, this represents a very unfortunate and difficult situation. Since this person is your friend, you will likely want the most favorable outcome for her. As such, you should tell your friend that if she intends to confront her boss about this, it is very likely that she'll been seen by others as a "chronic complainer." (pp. 62-63)

4. An exemplar is a concrete example of behavior that others have performed and is consistent with a given trait. An abstraction is a mental summary of someone that has been gleaned from repeated observations of their behavior. (p. 68)

5. The most commonly used tactic of other-enhancement is flattery (i.e., statements that praise the target person). A couple of additional tactics would include expressing agreement with the target person's views and doing small favors for him or her (pp. 69-70)

Chapter 3

Item Number	Practice Test 1	Practice Test 2	Practice Test 3	Comprehensive Test
1	A (p. 84)	D (p. 79)	A (p. 96)	D (p. 78)
2	B (p. 85)	A (p. 80)	C (pp. 98-99)	A (p. 80)
3	D (p. 85)	A (p. 82)	D (p. 98)	B (p. 80)
4	A (p. 86)	B (pp. 82-83)	B (pp. 101-102)	C (p. 82)
5	B (pp. 95-96)	C (p. 84)	C (p. 103)	C (pp. 85-86)
6	A (pp. 96-97)	B (pp. 86-87)	D (p. 104)	C (p. 87)
7	D (p. 97)	B (p. 90)	D (p. 105)	C (pp. 90-91)
8	C (pp 98-99)	D (p. 92)	C (pp. 106-107)	A (p. 92)
9	D (pp. 99-100)	B (pp. 94-95)	C (p. 109)	A (p. 95)
10	D (p. 105)	A (p. 95)	C (p. 79)	B (p. 99)
11				D (p. 102)
12				A (p. 104)
13				B (p. 105)
14				B (pp. 106-107)
15		*Correct Responses to*		B (p. 108)
16		*Short Answer/Essay Questions*		F (pp. 81-82)
17				T (p. 85)
18		↓		F (pp. 94-95)
19				F (p. 98)
20				F (p. 85)
21				T (p. 98)
22				T (p. 92)
23				T (p. 104)

1. There is no simple answer to this question; it depends on the measure of memory employed. In general, people report information consistent with their schemas, but, in fact, information inconsistent with schemas may be strongly present in memory, too. (pp. 81-82)

2. The representativeness heuristic is a strategy for making judgments based on the extent to which current stimuli or events resemble other stimuli or categories; the availability heuristic is used to make judgments on the basis of how easily specific kinds of information can be brought to mind. (pp. 85-86)

3. Due to the negativity bias, where we have a greater sensitivity to negative than positive information, you would likely recognize the threatening face first. (pp. 90-91)

4. The three principles of magical thinking are as follows. The law of contagion holds that when two objects touch, these pass properties to one another, and the effects of that contact may last well beyond the end of contact between these. The law of similarity suggests that things that resemble one another share basic properties. The third principle suggests that one's thoughts can influence the physical world in a manner not governed by the laws of physics. (pp. 97-98)

5. Affect can influence cognition in terms of its impact on memory. For instance, what we remember while in a given mood may be determined, in part, by what we learned when previously in that mood (mood-dependent memory). Our current moods—particularly if we are in a happy mood—can increase creativity since being in a happy mood activates a wider range of ideas. Also, information that evokes affective reactions may be processed differently than other kinds of information and thus, it may be impossible to ignore or disregard (mental contamination). For a more detailed overview of these processes, refer to pages 103-107 in your text.

Chapter 4

Item Number	Practice Test 1	Practice Test 2	Practice Test 3	Comprehensive Test
1	B (p. 130)	B (p. 118)	A (p. 138)	A (p. 121)
2	D (pp. 128-129)	B (p. 123)	B (p. 139)	B (p. 122)
3	A (pp. 130-132)	B (p. 125)	C (p. 140)	A (p. 124)
4	A (pp. 133-134)	B (p. 126)	B (p. 141)	D (p. 126)
5	B (pp. 137-138)	D (p. 130)	D (p. 143)	C (p. 128)
6	A (p. 138)	A (p. 131)	C (p. 144)	D (p. 131)
7	B (p. 138)	C (p. 132)	A (p. 145)	C (pp. 132-133)
8	C (p. 126)	A (pp. 132-133)	A (p. 150)	A (p. 137)
9	D (p. 141)	C (p. 134)	D (p. 150)	A (p. 138)
10	B (p. 152)	B (p. 137)	C (pp. 151-152)	D (p. 141)
11				A (p. 143)
12				B (pp. 145-146)
13				C (pp. 148-149)
14				B (p. 150)
15				C (p. 152)
16				F (p. 125)
17	*Correct Responses to*			F (p. 128)
18	*Short Answer/Essay Questions*			T (p. 132)
19				F (p. 137)
20	↓			F (p. 138)
21				T (p. 138)
22				F (p. 141)
23				F (p. 150)

1. Unlike classical conditioning, exposure to stimuli is below an individual's threshold of conscious awareness with respect to subliminal conditioning. (p. 122)

2. Attitudes serve at least five key functions: organizing and interpreting social information (knowledge), expressing our central values or beliefs (self-expression or self-identity), maintaining or enhancing our feelings of self-worth (self-esteem), helping people protect themselves from unwanted information about themselves (ego-defensive), and to make a good impression on others (impression motivation). (p. 126)

3. An event activates an attitude that influences our perceptions about the attitude object. Simultaneously, our knowledge of various social norms is activated. These factors shape our definition of the event and this perception, in turn, influences our behavior. (p. 134)

4. You should take a two-sided approach where both sides of the argument will be presented. (p. 137)

5. Dissonance can be used to generate hypocrisy. However, if you truly are going to be able to help your friend, he must publicly advocate the wearing of seat belts, must be induced to think about his own failures to wear his own seat belt in the past, and must be given access to direct means to reduce his dissonance. (p. 152)

Chapter 5

Item Number	Practice Test 1	Practice Test 2	Practice Test 3	Comprehensive Test
1	D (p. 161)	D (pp. 172-173)	B (p. 186)	D (p. 164)
2	C (p. 162-163)	C (p. 174)	C (p. 188)	B (p. 169)
3	B (p. 164)	B (p. 175)	B (pp. 190-191)	A (p. 171)
4	B (p. 164)	A (p. 175)	D (pp. 190-191)	D (pp. 172-173)
5	B (p. 166)	B (p. 176)	A (p. 190)	D (p. 174)
6	A (p. 166)	C (p. 177)	D (p. 192)	D (p. 179)
7	C (pp. 166-167)	A (pp. 179-180)	D (p. 192)	C (p. 184)
8	D (p. 169)	B (p. 180)	C (p. 195)	A (p. 186)
9	A (p. 170)	B (p. 184)	A (pp. 198-199)	A (pp. 190-191)
10	B (p. 171)	B (p. 185)	D (p. 200)	C (p. 192)
11				D (p. 199)
12				D (p. 180)
13				B (p. 165)
14		*Correct Responses to Short Answer/Essay Questions* ↓		C (p. 181)
15				B (p. 164)
16				F (pp. 167-168)
17				T (p. 164)
18				T (p. 169)
19				F (pp. 179-180)
20				F (p. 184)
21				F (pp. 190-191)
22				F (p. 192)
23				F (pp. 194-195)

1. Males and females describe themselves on dimensions involving concepts such as open- or broad-mindedness *and* passion and romance. However, women (unlike men) tend to have the negative schema of embarrassed/conservative that suggests anxiety and guilt in response to sex. Men often show a schema based on traits pertaining to power and aggression. (pp. 165-166)

2. You make an upward social comparison when you're comparing yourself to someone who's better off than you with respect to a certain attribute. Comparing yourself to a stranger tends to not effect self-

esteem since it simply isn't important to you. You might feel depressed and have lowered self-esteem if you compare yourself with someone in your in-group, though; basically, such a comparison suggests that you're not measuring up to your peers. However, comparing yourself with a close other will likely produce an assimilation effect and thus, increase your self-esteem. (p. 173)

3. Janet appears to be a high self-monitor. (pp. 179-180)

4. On the basis of this scale, the BSRI, a person could be a sex-typed masculine male or a feminine female; in such cases, these men and women are endorsing stereotypes consistent with their sex. An opposite pattern would be a reverse-typed feminine male or masculine female where such individuals are endorsing stereotypes inconsistent with their sex. Androgynous men and women possess a fairly equal blend of traditional masculine and feminine stereotypes. Undifferentiated men and women endorse few male or female stereotypes. (pp. 190-191)

5. Women continue to be more depressed than men. A key reason for this difference is a pervasive concern for how women look—particularly in terms of weight-related concerns. (pp. 199-200)

Chapter 6

Item Number	Practice Test 1	Practice Test 2	Practice Test 3	Comprehensive Test
1	C (p. 208)	C (pp. 218-219)	C (p. 232)	C (p. 209)
2	B (p. 209)	C (p. 221)	D (pp. 233-234)	C (p. 217)
3	A (pp. 210-211)	D (p. 222)	B (p. 235)	A (pp. 222-223)
4	C (p. 211)	A (p. 222)	B (p. 238)	A (p. 235)
5	B (p. 212)	D (p. 223)	A (p. 239)	B (p. 220)
6	D (pp. 213-214)	B (p. 223)	C (p. 241)	D (p. 245)
7	C (pp. 214-215)	A (pp. 226-227)	C (p. 241)	D (p. 215)
8	B (p. 215)	B (pp. 228-229)	D (pp. 245-246)	B (p. 214)
9	A (p. 217)	C (p. 229)	B (p. 246)	C (p. 216)
10	C (p. 217)	C (p. 230)	C (p. 245)	A (p. 217)
11				C (p. 220)
12				B (p. 229)
13				C (pp. 226-227)
14				B (p. 232)
15				D (p. 242)
16				T (p. 208)
17		*Correct Responses to*		F (p. 212)
18		*Short Answer/Essay Questions*		F (p. 217)
19				T (p. 220)
20		↓		T (p. 229)
21				F (pp. 218-220)
22				T (p. 245)
23				F (pp. 245-246)

[continued on next page]

1. Prejudice is a negative *attitude* toward the members of some group, whereas discrimination is a negative *action or behavior* toward the groups that are the targets of prejudice. (p. 209)

2. Realistic conflict theory postulates that prejudice often stems from direct competition between various social groups over scarce and valued resources. However, consistent with the hatred shown by Osama bin Laden and his followers, competition doesn't have to be real or direct to start this process. These individuals view the U.S. as a direct threat to their religion and culture—so, their end result is to demonize the U.S. and to try to destroy it as shown by the tragic events of September 11, 2001. (pp. 215-216)

3. We have a great deal of experience with members of our own group, so we're exposed to more variation within this group; typically, we have much less interactions with out-group members and likewise, we observe less variation within such groups. (p. 230)

4. Stereotype threat is a concern on the part of persons who are the target of stereotype that they'll be evaluated in terms of this stereotype. An example of empirical evidence in support of this phenomenon is that black undergraduates performed more poorly on a difficult cognitive task when their race was made salient and they believed that poor performance would confirm the cultural stereotype that blacks are less intelligent than whites; these effects didn't occur when race wasn't made salient. (p. 239)

5. Ida is indeed expressing sexist beliefs—specifically, benevolent sexism. (p. 241)

Chapter 7

Item Number	Practice Test 1	Practice Test 2	Practice Test 3	Comprehensive Test
1	D (p. 255)	A (p. 267)	C (pp. 276-277)	C (pp. 258-259)
2	B (p. 256)	B (pp. 268-269)	B (p. 278)	C (p. 260)
3	A (p. 257)	B (p. 269)	C (p. 279)	D (pp. 261-262)
4	B (p. 257)	C (p. 271)	C (p. 280)	D (p. 278)
5	B (p. 260)	A (p. 271)	A (p. 281)	D (p. 286)
6	C (pp. 260-261)	D (p. 272)	D (p. 282)	A (p. 285)
7	C (p. 262)	C (p. 273)	D (p. 283)	A (p. 286)
8	A (p. 262)	D (p. 273)	B (p. 284)	B (p. 290)
9	B (pp. 263-264)	B (p. 275)	D (p. 285)	B (p. 256)
10	D (p. 265)	C (p. 276)	A (p. 287)	B (p. 265)
11				A (p. 269)
12				C (p. 272)
13				C (pp. 274-276)
14				D (p. 278)
15				B (pp. 283-284)
16		*Correct Responses to*		T (p. 257)
17		*Short Answer/Essay Questions*		F (p. 257)
18				F (p. 271)
19		↓		F (p. 286)
20				T (p. 285)
21				F (p. 273)
22				F (p. 268)
23				T (p. 290)

1. Some examples of how repeated exposures and proximity function in natural settings include evidence that students are more likely to become acquainted or friends if they sit next to each other in class. It is plausible that attraction could cause proximity or that some third variable could cause both. However, there is empirical evidence showing that when students are randomly assigned to apartments in a college setting, proximity continues to play a key role in attraction. Thus, it is still accurate to conclude that proximity causes liking even in natural settings. (pp. 260-261)

2. The need for affiliation is a basic motive to seek and maintain interpersonal relationships. Some people prefer to be alone most, some, or hardly none of the time—this pertains to their relatively stable disposition or traits. However, certain settings or situations (e.g., having surgery, experiencing a disaster) may motivate an individual to seek out others—this pertains to the temporary states of this need. (p. 268)

3. Physical attractiveness is often viewed as a sign of health, youth, and fertility—particularly in women. (p. 273)

4. They will be in a state of imbalance and can restore balance by either changing or the other's attitudes, misperceiving the degree of dissimilarity, or (in a worst case scenario) simply deciding not to like each other. (p. 285)

5. The repulsion hypothesis is that attraction isn't increased by similar attitudes but only decreased by dissimilar ones. This hypothesis is inaccurate in its prediction that similarity is not relevant to attraction—clearly it is. However, it did contain a partial truth in the sense that we tend to like those we meet until we discover too many areas of dissimilarity. (p. 286)

Chapter 8

Item Number	Practice Test 1	Practice Test 2	Practice Test 3	Comprehensive Test
1	D (p. 299)	D (p. 312)	A (p. 329)	C (p. 311)
2	A (p. 300)	D (p. 313)	B (p. 331)	A (pp. 327-328)
3	C (p. 302)	C (p. 317)	B (p. 332)	D (p. 333)
4	D (p. 303)	D (p. 319)	C (p. 334)	A (pp. 320-321)
5	B (p. 304)	C (p. 322)	B (p. 334)	D (p. 333)
6	B (p. 306)	C (p. 324)	D (p. 335)	D (p. 304)
7	A (p. 306)	A (p. 324)	D (pp. 337-338)	C (p. 306)
8	D (pp. 308-309)	D (p. 326)	B (p. 338)	B (p. 310)
9	A (p. 309)	B (p. 326)	A (p. 339)	D (p. 314)
10	B (pp. 310-311)	C (p. 328)	B (p. 340)	C (p. 323)
11				A (p. 324)
12				C (p. 337)
13				A (p. 336)
14				A (p. 336)
15				B (pp. 339-340)
16		*Correct Responses to Short Answer/Essay Questions* ↓		T (p. 340)
17				T (pp. 328-329)
18				T (p. 304)
19				F (p. 314)
20				F (p. 303)
21				T (p. 341)
22				T (p. 331)
23				F (pp. 330-331)

1. Chris appears to have a dismissing attachment style. (p. 310)

2. The two primary interventions for loneliness are cognitive therapy and social skills training. Cognitive therapy teaches individuals to disrupt the pattern of negative self-evaluations and to encourage new positive cognitions about the self. Since so many lonely people have poor social skills, social skills training allows individuals to learn how to successfully interact with others. (p. 314)

3. Bret appears to be feeling passionate love. (p. 320)

4. Those with an unrestricted sociosexual orientation tend to be male and often feel that members of the opposite sex are sought simply as sex partners without any need for closeness or emotional bonding. Those with a restricted sociosexual orientation tend to be female and believe that a sexual relationship is acceptable only when accompanied by affection and tenderness. (p. 326)

5. Overall, companionate love (e.g., sharing activities, working together, laughing) appears to be the key ingredient for a successful marriage. However, women also show even greater happiness in the marriage if they continue to feel a sense of passionate love as well. (p. 333)

Chapter 9

Item Number	Practice Test 1	Practice Test 2	Practice Test 3	Comprehensive Test
1	B (p. 348)	D (p. 366)	B (p. 375)	C (p. 352)
2	D (p. 349)	C (p. 366)	D (p. 375)	C (p. 349)
3	C (p. 351)	D (p. 367)	B (p. 376)	A (p. 350)
4	D (p. 353)	B (p. 368)	D (p. 376)	A (p. 376)
5	B (p. 354)	B (p. 369)	C (p. 376)	D (p. 348)
6	B (p. 356)	A (p. 370)	C (p. 377)	A (p. 348)
7	A (p. 358)	D (p. 370)	C (pp. 378-379)	A (p. 351)
8	C (p. 362)	C (p. 371)	A (p. 379)	D (p. 377)
9	D (pp. 363-364)	D (p. 372)	A (p. 380)	C (pp. 377-378)
10	A (p. 364)	D (pp. 373-374)	B (p. 380)	D (p. 348)
11				B (pp. 356-357)
12				C (p. 365)
13				C (p. 368)
14				B (p. 371)
15		*Correct Responses to*		B (p. 380)
16		*Short Answer/Essay Questions*		T (pp. 358-359)
17				F (p. 351)
18		↓		F (p. 352)
19				T (p. 369)
20				F (p. 372)
21				T (p. 371)
22				F (pp. 376-377)
23				F (p. 378)

1. Mary is showing conformity. (p. 348)

2. Cultures of honor, which are typically found in U.S. West and South, are cultures in which strong social norms condone violence as a means of answering an affront to one's honor. (pp. 356-357)

3. The three key are: the minority view must be consistent, the minority shouldn't appear rigid or dogmatic, and their views should be consistent with the general social climate. (pp. 363-364)

4. This is an example of the "that's-not-all" technique. (p. 369)

5. Milgram reran his initial study in a run-down office building in a nearby city and not at Yale University; the overall obedience level of 65% was unchanged by this change in location. However, he did note a decline in obedience (at the highest shock level) when the research participant had to grasp the victim's hand and place it on a metal shock plate; here 30% of his subjects showed total obedience. (p. 377)

Chapter 10

Item Number	Practice Test 1	Practice Test 2	Practice Test 3	Comprehensive Test
1	C (p. 389)	B (p. 406)	C (pp. 414-415)	A (p. 391)
2	C (pp. 390-391)	C (p. 408)	A (p. 415)	A (pp. 390-391)
3	C (p. 391)	B (p. 409)	A (p. 418)	A (pp. 410-411)
4	C (pp. 393-394)	D (p. 410)	D (p. 419)	B (p. 414)
5	A (p. 394)	B (p. 411)	D (p. 419)	C (p. 425)
6	B (p. 393)	A (p. 411)	B (p. 422)	B (p. 409)
7	C (pp. 398-399)	A (p. 412)	A (p. 424)	A (p. 425)
8	D (p. 402)	D (p. 412)	D (p. 425)	C (p. 425)
9	A (p. 403)	A (p. 412)	A (p. 426)	C (p. 396)
10	B (p. 404)	C (p. 414)	C (pp. 426-427)	D (p. 403)
11				B (pp. 406-407)
12				C (p. 409)
13				D (p. 413)
14				C (p. 417)
15				D (p. 419)
16		*Correct Responses to*		F (p. 397)
17		*Short Answer/Essay Questions*		F (p. 406)
18				T (p. 416)
19		↓		T (p. 414)
20				F (p. 425)
21				F (p. 411)
22				F (p. 412)
23				F (p. 427)

1. In order for a bystander to engage in helping behavior, he or she must do all of the following behaviors in the following order: attend to the situation, interpret the situation as an emergency, assume responsibility for taking action, have the knowledge, skills, or training to provide help, and decide to engage in helping behavior. If *any* of these stages are not followed through, help will not be given. (pp. 393-398)

2. Some shows and characters, such as *Sesame Street*, have clear prosocial models where children are taught the values of kindness and helping behavior; these shows really do appear to increase children's prosocial behavior. However, violent media (such as violent games like "Street Fighter") tend to decrease prosocial behavior. More research needs to be conducted with respect to characters and shows like *The Simpsons* that feature models that aren't violent yet are unconcerned with the

plight of others; the text authors conclude that such shows and characters likely have a negative effect on children and their likelihood of showing prosocial behavior. (pp. 401-402)

3. Regardless of whether an emergency is ambiguous, people who are in a good mood don't like to engage in behaviors that could threaten that mood. As such, if they perceive such a threat, they likely will not help. (p. 406)

4. Generativity is an adult's concern for and commitment to the well-being of future generations. Thus, by volunteering, an adult may feel as though he or she is allowing for the development of a better society. (p. 416)

5. In general, this model predicts that you would be most likely to help a close biological relative—particularly to younger fertile relatives (especially women) since they are the key to reproductive success. (pp. 426-427)

Chapter 11

Item Number	Practice Test 1	Practice Test 2	Practice Test 3	Comprehensive Test
1	C (p. 435)	A (pp. 449-450)	D (p. 460)	C (p. 434)
2	A (p. 436)	B (p. 440)	D (p. 460)	C (pp. 435-436)
3	B (p. 437)	B (p. 451)	C (p. 461)	A (p. 435)
4	C (pp. 437-438)	D (p. 451)	B (p. 462)	B (p. 454)
5	C (p. 440)	C (p. 453)	A (p. 463)	C (p. 463)
6	D (p. 443)	C (p. 454)	D (p. 464)	A (p. 440)
7	A (p. 443)	B (p. 455)	C (p. 464)	D (pp. 449-450)
8	B (p. 446)	B (p. 457)	B (p. 465)	D (p. 467)
9	B (p. 447)	B (p. 458)	B (p. 466)	D (p. 442)
10	D (p. 448)	A (pp. 458-459)	A (p. 467)	C (p. 456)
11				B (p. 446)
12				C (p. 459)
13				C (p. 461)
14				B (pp. 436-437)
15				A (p. 435)
16		*Correct Responses to Short Answer/Essay Questions* ↓		F (p. 460)
17				F (p. 448)
18				T (pp. 454-455)
19				F (pp. 451-452)
20				F (p. 440)
21				F (p. 464)
22				F (p. 437)
23				F (p. 451)

1. The two main categories of GAAM are input variables (such as some kind of attack from another person or the presence of cues associated with aggression) and individual differences (such as specific skills related to aggression or certain values about violence). (pp. 437-438)

2. The Type A behavior pattern consists of high levels of competitiveness, time urgency, and hostility. (pp. 449-450)

3. Low aggressors become more aggressive when intoxicated and high aggressors become slightly less aggressive when intoxicated. (p. 456)

4. The three main categories of aggression in the workplace are: expressions of hostility (e.g., behaviors that are primarily verbal or symbolic in nature), obstructionism (e.g., behaviors designed to impede the target's performance), and overt aggression (e.g., physical assault, theft). (p. 461)

5. Pete is using the incompatible response technique. He should use this with care since it sometimes backfires when the target person is very angry—but if a person isn't already enraged, it can be an effective way to reduce or prevent aggression or anger. So again, it may work—it all depends on how enraged Josh feels. (p. 467)

Chapter 12

Item Number	Practice Test 1	Practice Test 2	Practice Test 3	Comprehensive Test
1	A (pp. 475-476)	D (p. 486)	D (p. 495)	C (p. 477)
2	B (p. 476)	D (p. 487)	A (p. 496)	A (p. 480)
3	D (p. 477)	B (p. 487)	B (p. 499)	C (p. 482)
4	A (p. 478)	A (p. 488)	B (p. 499)	C (p. 486)
5	C (p. 479)	D (p. 489)	B (p. 502)	C (p. 502)
6	C (p. 480)	C (pp. 490-491)	C (pp. 504-505)	C (p. 502)
7	A (p. 482)	A (p. 491)	A (p. 507)	B (p. 507)
8	D (p. 482)	C (p. 492)	C (p. 509)	A (p. 508)
9	A (p. 484)	A (p. 493)	C (p. 510)	A (p. 509)
10	B (p. 485)	A (p. 493)	C (p. 511)	A (pp. 510-511)
11				A (p. 490)
12				D (p. 491)
13				B (p. 476)
14				D (pp. 478-479)
15				D (p. 497)
16		*Correct Responses to*		T (pp. 484-485)
17		*Short Answer/Essay Questions*		F (p. 502)
18				T (p. 486)
19		↓		T (p. 488)
20				F (p. 479)
21				F (p. 508)
22				F (p. 507)
23				F (p. 509)

1. Groups function due to the presence of roles, status, norms, and cohesiveness. Roles allow individuals to know their specific duties within the group. Status enables the development of leaders through the importance of position and rank. Norms provide the general rules for how a group should

behave. Cohesiveness pertains to a variety of factors that encourage the group to stay together. (pp. 477-480)

2. Expectancy-valence theory suggests that individuals will work hard on a given task only to the extent that the following conditions exist: (1) They believe that working hard will lead to better performance (expectancy), (2) they believe that better performance will be recognized and rewarded (instrumentality), and (3) the rewards obtained are ones they value and desire (valence). (p. 487)

3. A major social factor that creates conflict is faulty attributions; these are errors concerning the causes behind others' behavior. Another factor is faulty communication, whereby communication is relayed in a manner that angers or annoys a person even if that was not the intention; in this respect, destructive criticism leaves the recipient hungry for revenge. A third social cause of conflict involves the tendency to perceive our own views as objective and as reflecting reality, but those of others are biased by their ideology. (p. 496)

4. This example illustrates distributive justice. (p. 502)

5. Social decision schemes are rules relating to the initial distribution of members' views to final group decisions. The majority-wins rule suggests that the group often opts for whatever position is initially supported by most of its members. The truth-wins rule suggests that the correct decision will ultimately be accepted as its correctness is recognized by more and more members. The first-shift rule is the tendency for groups to adopt a decision consistent with the direction of the first shift in opinion shown by any member. (p. 507)

Chapter 13

Item Number	Practice Test 1	Practice Test 2	Practice Test 3	Comprehensive Test
1	A (p. 520)	C (p. 538)	B (p. 550)	B (pp. 525-527)
2	D (p. 521)	A (p. 538)	A (p. 551)	A (p. 530)
3	B (p. 521)	A (p. 539)	B (p. 552)	D (p. 532)
4	C (p. 524)	B (p. 541)	D (p. 553)	C (p. 532)
5	D (p. 525)	C (p. 542)	C (p. 556)	B (p. 534)
6	B (p. 527)	D (pp. 543-544)	A (p. 557)	B (p. 540)
7	B (p. 528)	D (p. 545)	C (pp. 557-558)	D (p. 540)
8	C (pp. 530-531)	A (p. 546)	D (p. 559)	B (p. 541)
9	D (p. 536)	C (p. 547)	C (p. 560)	C (p. 543)
10	A (p. 537)	B (p. 548)	B (p. 561)	B (p. 543)
11				D (p. 549)
12				B (p. 551)
13				A (p. 554)
14				C (p. 557)
15		*Correct Responses to Short Answer/Essay Questions* ↓		A (p. 560)
16				F (p. 548)
17				T (p. 539)
18				F (p. 543)
19				T (pp. 531-532)
20				F (pp. 535-536)
21				T (p. 551)
22				F (pp. 553-554)
23				F (p. 559)

1. Eyewitness testimony can be improved through a blank-lineup control, which is a procedure in which a witness views a police lineup that doesn't include a suspect. If a witness doesn't identify a suspect, this increases confidence in their testimony; however, if he or she identifies an innocent person, they're told of the mistake and cautioned to be more careful. Either way, this increases accuracy. Also, encouraging witnesses to give first impressions and to show the lineup one person at a time, rather than as a group enhances eyewitness testimony. (pp. 530-531)

2. Direct and indirect effects of stress each lead to an increase in illness. The indirect effects occur when the negative emotional effects of stress interfere with health-related behavior, such as eating a balanced diet or scheduling a physical examination. The direct physical effects of stress involves the delay of healing process in wounds and negative effects on the endocrine and immune system. (p. 542)

3. Awkward attempts to provide comfort can make things worse; some examples include minimizing the problem, suggesting that the problem is due to the stressed person's fault, and bumbling efforts to help. (p. 548)

4. When individuals feel that they're being treated fairly by their organization, they're more likely to engage in citizenship behavior than when they feel that they're being treated unfairly. In other words, why go that extra mile to help out your organization if your organization doesn't treat you with some degree of equity and fairness? (p. 554)

5. Charisma doesn't appear to matter in stable, unchanging environments. However, in a rapidly changing, chaotic environments, companies who had high charisma leaders outperformed those with low charisma leaders. (p. 561)